THE INSTITUTION OF CIVIL ENGINEERS

Construction research and development

VOL. 2. MARKET SECTOR PRIORITIES

Report of the ICE Research Sub-Committee
December 1986

THOMAS TELFORD, LONDON

CONSTRUCTION RESEARCH AND DEVELOPMENT REPORTS

VOLUME 1. Organisation and funding.

VOLUME 2. Market sector priorities.

VOLUME 3. Background information to Volume 2. (Volume 3 has not been published and is lodged for reference in the Library of the Institution of Civil Engineers, 1-7 Great George Street, London SW1P 3AA. Telephone: 01-222 7722)

Published for The Institution of Civil Engineers by Thomas Telford Ltd, P.O. Box 101, 26-34 Old Street, London EC1P 1JH

First published 1986

ISBN 0 7277 0384 6

© The Institution of Civil Engineers, 1986

Typeset by Opus Magazines Ltd, London EC1

Printed in England by Imediaprint Ltd

ICE RESEARCH SUB-COMMITTEE

It is not always appreciated that the construction industry, in common with most others, is dependent upon innovation, research and development in order to meet increasingly stringent standards at home and to enable it to compete successfully abroad.

Further, in the construction industry particularly, the results of research need careful evaluation and validation and dissemination in forms usable by practising engineers, if maximum benefit is to be obtained from investment in R&D.

There are many competent research organisations in the field of construction but they are predominantly supported by public sector funding. The Institution of Civil Engineers believes that the industry itself should become more involved in the selection and funding of research and in its implementation, and that to achieve the best results it is essential to establish a national co-ordinating body which would recognise the partnership between the industry, the public sector including Government, and the research organisations themselves.

The Institution has always considered research to be an important interest. It played a principal role in establishing CIRIA and made a major contribution to the Task Force Report in 1981. It now proposes to establish a permanent Research Sub-Committee and offers its assistance in helping to establish research priorities. This will not, however, be enough. It looks to Government to establish the framework within which research investment in construction can become more rewarding to both client and the industry and more beneficial to the nation.

D.A.D. Reeve
ICE President, 1985-86
4 November 1986

ICE RESEARCH SUB-COMMITTEE MEMBERS

CONTENTS

1.   INTRODUCTION

The report, 'Long-Term Research and Development Requirements in Civil Engineering', commonly referred to as the Task Force Report, was prepared jointly by the Institution of Civil Engineers and CIRIA in 1981 for the Department of the Environment, the Department of Transport and the Science and Engineering Research Council (SERC). Based on the market demands and opportunities at that time, the Report identified some 200 high priority R&D requirements to meet the needs of practitioners in the foreseeable future — that is, for 20 years or so. The Report also gave critical comment on the national organisation and funding arrangements for civil engineering R&D and made recommendations for improvement. Among the Task Force's conclusions was the recommendation that the long-term R&D requirements and the organisational structure should be reviewed periodically.

The Institution's Research Sub-Committee was appointed in 1985 to undertake, among other duties, a review of the Task Force Report in the light of present circumstances and to prepare any revisions that might be necessary.

The Sub-Committee's review of funding and organisational arrangements is presented in Volume 1. In Volume 2, an appraisal is made of the construction market in the UK and overseas; and for each of the seven broad 'market' areas in which civil engineering plays a dominant part, an assessment is given of changes occurring, future needs, the effects of recent innovations and advances in other technologies. Each chapter devoted to a specific market area includes a list of high priority R&D requirements identified from this review.

To facilitate comparison with the Task Force's R&D recommendations, the final chapter in this Volume presents extracts from the Task Force's summary of R&D requirements within the seven subject areas (e.g. materials, structures, geotechnics) used in that Report, together with a commentary on each, based on the findings of this present review.

2. METHOD OF REVIEW

The 1981 Task Force Report involved the preparation of thirty-nine papers on Products (Market) sectors, and twenty-eight papers on Discipline (Technology) areas. These papers have been reviewed, by the original authors in most cases, and the papers, together with their reviews, form Volume 3, which will be lodged for reference in the Library of the Institution of Civil Engineers.

For the purpose of distilling the findings of these papers, seven broad market sectors were selected as listed in this Volume. Each Institution Group Board has reviewed those papers which relate to its respective market sector and techniques.

The section on buildings was a special case as this market sector involves many disciplines outside civil engineering. The Chartered Institution of Building Services Engineers had agreed to one of its members joining the Sub-Committee. However, as the work developed, the assistance of other disciplines was sought and the Structural Engineering Group Board consulted some other Institutions for views.

As a result of the rapidly changing market in civil engineering over the last ten years, together with different rates of change in various market sectors, this review of research needs begins with a chapter on Construction Market Appraisal. However, it was not found to be possible within the limited time and resources available to the Sub-Committee to allocate priorities between market sectors. This duty should form one of the early tasks of the co-ordinating body recommended elsewhere in the Report.

In the lists of R&D needs that are presented at the end of the Group Board Reports in Chapters 4 – 11, items currently regarded as being of the highest priority are given in italics. More than 200 items have been identified in this category, many of them being similar to those identified by the Task Force, but others are new requirements reflecting the changes in demands and events in recent years.

Bearing in mind the short time-scale of this review, it cannot be claimed that the lists of R&D requirements are complete. However, they do provide ample evidence of the need for a substantially increased civil engineering R&D effort if the industry is to improve its efficiency in meeting present and future demands in the UK, and to maintain or, in some cases, to regain its competitiveness in overseas markets.

3. THE MARKET FOR CONSTRUCTION

3.1. Introduction

This chapter gives an overall view of the size and present trends of the construction market in both the UK and overseas, for UK contractors, consultants and suppliers. Each of the following chapters will discuss, for the market sector or discipline concerned, particular features of the existing market, likely future needs and the research requirements for that factor or discipline.

After summarising the present overall position and recent past trends, this chapter will attempt to identify a number of the key factors affecting the future of the construction market, and the implication these will have on research requirements for the industry as a whole. In order to do this, it is necessary to consider the statistics that are available for both UK and overseas work. These statistics vary widely in their origins, soundness and detail but are sufficient to give the general background for further discussions and development. To avoid confusion such statistics have been kept to the minimum necessary and are drawn from three main sources:

(a) UK Government, NEDO and EEC data

(b) Published data in surveys conducted by Engineering News Record

(c) The Association of Consulting Engineers.

3.2. The UK market

The present state of the UK construction market can be seen by examining Table 1 and Figs 1 – 4 which are taken from the National Economic Development Offices, 'Construction Forecasts 1986-1987', June 1986.

These statistics, when considered in constant money values, show the major decline in new construction work that took place in the UK in the 1970s and early 1980s, the increasing volume of repair, maintenance and refurbishing work, and a forecast of a very slowly increasing volume of new construction in the next few years; they do not indicate a major future recovery in the fortunes of the industry. Civil engineering has been particularly affected, as can be seen from Figs 2 and 3. Building has not suffered such a severe decline owing to a repairs and maintenance business and also to a growing private commercial market (Fig. 4).

3.3. The overseas market for UK firms

The position in the overseas market can be seen from Tables 2 and 3. While statistics for overseas work cannot be regarded as completely reliable, on account of the methods by which they are collected, they do show certain trends. The two main trends are, not unexpectedly, that with the decline of the oil market and the completion of many large infrastructure projects in the Middle East, the volume of available work is falling and, more importantly, there are also signs of UK contractors and consultants losing market share. If the figures are considered in real value terms, the decline in the available market is even more striking.

One further interesting set of statistics is that produced by the Association of Consulting Engineers, which gives capital value of work

Table 1. Construction output and forecasts 1976–1988 (£ million)

	Actual										Forecast*		
	1976	1977	1978	1979	1980	1981	1982	1983	1984	1985†	1986	1987	1988
Housing:													
Public	2970 (+10)	2702 (−9)	2539 (−6)	2108 (−17)	1711 (−19)	1124 (−34)	940 (−16)	1001 (+6)	910 (−9)	751 (−17)	650 (−13)	575 (−12)	525 (−9)
Private	3318 (+7)	3142 (−5)	3558 (+13)	3283 (−8)	2585 (−21)	2351 (−9)	2701 (+15)	3238 (+20)	3118 (−3)	2966 (−5)	3275 (+10)	3325 (+2)	3250 (−2)
Other:													
Public	4641 (−1)	4425 (−5)	4238 (−4)	3905 (−8)	3524 (−10)	3343 (−5)	3493 (+4)	3556 (+2)	3599 (+1)	3413 (−5)	3345 (−2)	3345 (nc)	3380 (+1)
Private Industrial	2276 (−4)	2638 (+16)	2803 (+6)	3004 (+7)	2806 (−7)	2339 (−17)	2100 (−10)	1879 (−11)	2354 (+25)	2711 (+15)	2440 (−10)	2415 (−1)	2510 (+4)
Private Commercial	2268 (−12)	2268 (nc)	2520 (+11)	2390 (−5)	2430 (+2)	2601 (+7)	2957 (+14)	3014 (+2)	3147 (+4)	3367 (+7)	3635 (+8)	3815 (+5)	3890 (+2)
Total new work	15473 (nc)	15175 (−2)	15658 (+3)	14689 (−6)	13055 (−11)	11758 (−10)	12190 (+4)	12688 (+4)	13128 (+3)	13208 (+1)	13345 (+1)	13475 (+1)	13555 (+0·5)
Repair and maintenance	6228 (−6)	6442 (+3·5)	7451 (+15·5)	8570 (+15)	8997 (+5)	8189 (−9)	8069 (−1)	8413 (+4)	8693 (+3·5)	8912 (+2·5)	9170 (+3)	9420 (+2·5)	9625 (+2)
Total all work	21701 (−1·5)	21617 (−0·5)	23109 (+7)	23260 (+0·5)	22052 (−5)	19947 (−10)	20260 (+1·5)	21101 (+4)	21821 (+3·5)	22120 (+1·5)	22515 (+2)	22895 (+1·5)	23180 (+1)

* Forecast figures have been rounded to the nearest £5 million.
† Provisional figures.
Percentage annual changes over previous year shown in brackets.

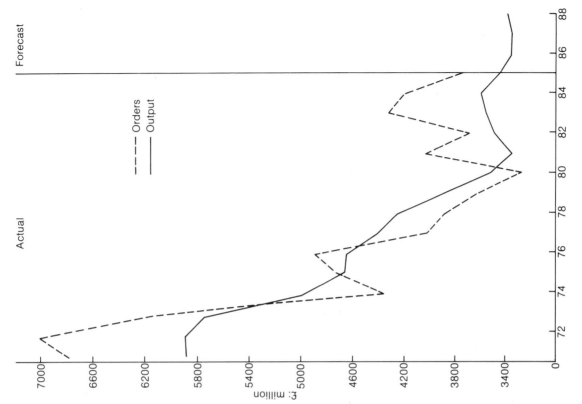

Fig. 2. Public non-housing output and orders at 1980 prices

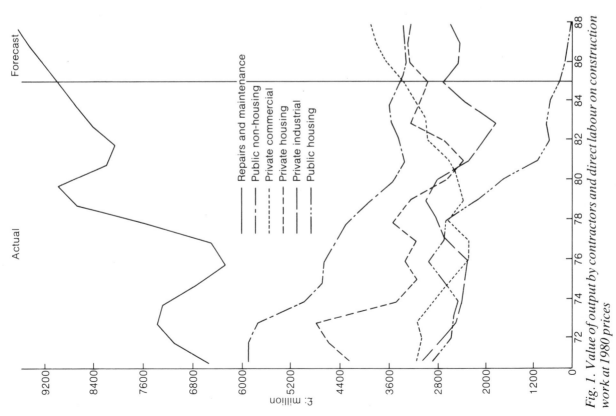

Fig. 1. Value of output by contractors and direct labour on construction work at 1980 prices

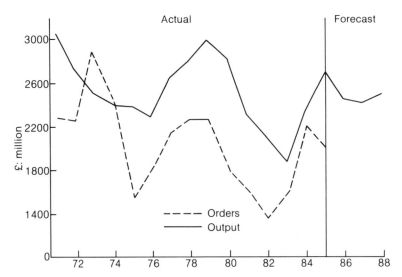

Fig. 3. Industrial output and orders at 1980 prices

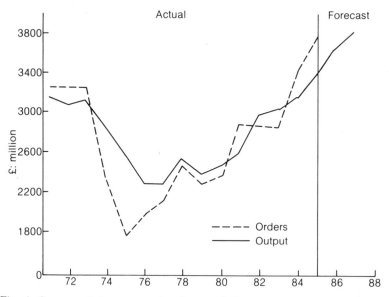

Fig. 4. Commercial output and orders at 1980 prices

Table 2. *UK contractors' world market share*

	Billions of US dollars					
	1980	1981	1982	1983	1984	1985
a) Total orders received by top 200 firms	108·3	129·9	123·1	93·6	80·5	na*
b) Orders received by UK firms	5·2	8·8	7·5	6·4	5·6	na
Share a/b	4·8%	6·8%	6·1%	6·8%	6·8%	na

*na = not available.
Source: *Engineering News Record.*

Table 3. *UK consultants' world market share*

	Billions of US dollars					
	1980	1981	1982	1983	1984	1985
a) Value of billings of international design firms	2·658	3·068	3·737	3·800	3·464	na*
b) Value of billings of UK firms	0·408	0·393	0·514	0·592	0·454	na
Share a/b	15·3%	12·8%	13·8%	15·4%	13·1%	na

*na = not available.
Source: *Engineering News Record.*

Table 4. *ACE member firms' work in hand overseas (capital costs in £ million)*

Type of Work	1982		1983		1984		1985	
	Value	%	Value	%	Value	%	Value	%
Roads, bridges, tunnels	7809	15	6176	13	6226	13	6689	14
Structural – Commercial	10411	20*	9976	21*	7184	15	6425	13
Railways	4165	8	3800	8	2874	6	6099	12
Thermal power stations	4685	9	3800	8	3831	8	4181	8
Water supply	4165	8	3800	8	3352	7	3734	8
Irrigation	1041	2	1425	3	1916	4	3707	8
Drainage, sewage and refuse disposal	4685	9	3563	7·5	4302	9	2893	6
Harbours, docks and sea defences	4165	8	3325	7	2396	5	2266	5
Electrical and mechanical services	2082	4	2613	5·5	2874	6	2147	4
Chemical, petroleum, gas	1562	3	2138	4·5	1916	4	2094	4
Airports	1562	3	950	2	1438	3	1923	4
Structural – Industrial	inc.* above		inc.* above		1438	3	1730	4
Land planning and developments	1562	3	1900	4	1438	3	1336	3
Power transmission	1562	3	1663	3·5	1916	4	1296	3
Hydro-electric	1562	3	1900	4	2395	5	579	1
Desalination	521	1	238	0·5	958	2	384	1
Nuclear power	521	1	238	0·5	—	—	156	—
Miscellaneous					1438	3	1624	3
Total	52060	100	47505	100	47892	100	49263	100

* Structural, commercial and industrial grouped together.

overseas on which UK consulting engineers are engaged (Table 4). These statistics also indicate the extent and type of work overseas that becomes available to contractors. Furthermore, they confirm the recent decline in the overseas market for both UK contractors and consultants, and also some significant shifts in the type of work. For example, the increase in the percentage share of irrigation and railway projects and the decrease in hydro-electric works and harbour works should be noted.

3.4.   The main factors

The factors affecting future demand for construction are many, various, interdependent and conflicting. They include:

(a) political decisions by government

(b) economic and financial factors: the general level of economic prosperity or otherwise, including changes in Gross National Product, interest rates, investment climate, etc.

(c) social requirements and expectations; public or political demand for improved services and infrastructure

(d) population growth or decline and population movement, e.g. from rural to city environments

(e) technological developments; exploitation of new resources, materials and methods.

This report is primarily concerned with item (e), but technological research and development is driven and influenced by the other factors. As examples, the investment put into research and development will be adversely affected if the margins earned by the construction industry are forced down too far by lack of public and private investment and consequent increased competition. Public investment is controlled by political decision, as has been the case in the UK over the past few years. Political decisions are in turn controlled by public demand, needs and expectations.

These needs and expectations are, where increases in the standard of living have taken place as over the past few decades, becoming increasingly important factors. As an example, the availability of transportation systems that are reasonably efficient is taken for granted by the public in the developed countries of the world; however, they have tolerance limits in respect of excessive delays. Similarly, there is a general expectation that power, water and sewerage services will not be interrupted. These developments of public opinion should influence both future Government expenditure and private development proposals, with consequent improvement in the market for construction in the UK.

Overseas, such needs are overshadowed by economic problems and, in too many places, by the struggle for mere existence. Nevertheless, the developing areas of the world now also have considerable expectations and these must have some beneficial effect on the market for construction, small though it may be at present.

The result, therefore, is what should be a balanced system of interacting forces; the balance is constantly changing and the overall position can at times approach instability, as is probably the case at present with regard to the state of the UK infrastructure and housing stock, or can become completely unstable as has happened in the disaster areas of Africa.

Civil engineering, and the construction industry as a whole, has to rely on this balance of forces being maintained if the state of the industry's health is to be kept in good shape. The industry can encourage investment in its markets but only if it can respond to the expressed needs in an efficient and cost-effective manner; this requires adequate and continuing investment in new techniques and developments.

3.5.   Future trends

3.5.1.   United Kingdom

The UK continues to invest less in new construction than any other country in Western Europe, as can be seen in Table 5. However, there are now some signs of improvement in construction investment in the UK, owing to three of the main factors listed above.

The economic and financial factors, such as low inflation and falling interest rates, are helpful in creating an improved climate for investment, but these must be balanced by the long-term effect of oil prices, the costs to the nation of unemployment, and the impending decline in North Sea oil output. In the short term there could, therefore, be an improvement but the longer term outlook is not optimistic.

Politically and socially, there is growing pressure on Government for increased expenditure on improving the state of the nation's infrastructure, schools and hospitals, and, perhaps and hopefully, a growing awareness of the need to invest as a preparation for a future without North Sea oil.

There are also signs that the number of major construction projects may increase somewhat by the use of private financing. Typical examples are the Channel Tunnel, the Dartford Crossing and the Mersey and Severn Barrages. If this country could find a politically acceptable method of combining public and private funding, as is the situation in the USA, it would be of great benefit to the nation as a whole.

The conclusion must, therefore, be that there are grounds for cautious optimism, particularly in the areas of:

– refurbishing existing facilities and housing

– energy conservation

– energy, particularly coal and tidal power but with a major question mark hanging over nuclear power for some years to come

– infrastructure repair and development, particularly in water and sewerage.

Table 5.   Investment in new construction

	Housing as % of GDP			Non-housing as % of GDP			All construction as % of GDP		
	1982	1983	1984	1982	1983	1984	1982	1983	1984
Belgium	3·4	3·3	na*	7·8	na	na	11·2	na	na
Denmark	3·6	4·3	5·1	5·7	5·3	5·0	9·3	9·6	10·1
France	5·5	5·2	4·8	5·6	5·3	5·0	11·1	10·5	9·8
Germany	6·2	6·3	6·3	6·5	6·2	6·1	12·7	12·5	12·4
Ireland	5·5	na	na	9·1	na	na	14·6	12·8	11·8
Italy	5·3	5·1	na	6·0	6·0	na	11·3	11·1	10·9
The Netherlands	5·3	5·2	5·1	5·6	5·2	na	10·9	10·4	na
United Kingdom	3·4	3·5	3·8	5·5	5·2	5·4	8·9	8·7	9·2
Norway	4·9	4·2	3·7	11·1	12·7	14·4	16·0	16·9	18·1
Sweden	4·3	4·0	3·8	6·6	6·4	6·2	10·9	10·4	10·0
Switzerland	na	na	na	na	na	na	16·2	16·1	15·9
Canada	3·7	4·2	3·8	10·8	9·1	8·5	14·5	13·3	12·3
United States	2·9	4·0	4·1	6·2	na	na	9·1	na	na

* na = not available.
Source: *UN Annual Bulletin of Housing and Building Statistics for Europe.*

3.5.2.   *Overseas*

The position concerning the overseas market is not easy to forecast. The present falling trend in demand will not be reversed until oil prices recover considerably, or there is increased investment or aid across the North/South Divide of the richer and poorer nations. The Middle East market is falling as major development is completed. The Far East is still (relatively) in a development phase but is being held back by world-wide economic problems. Africa will continue to be the poorest continent with its apparently unsolvable difficulties of population growth, low commodity prices and underproduction of food.

The conclusion here must, therefore, be that the future market for UK companies overseas will continue to decline unless there is a major change in international relations, technology or the world economic situation. The strongest of the markets available are in areas such as:

– water, irrigation and drainage

– agriculture

– communicatons — road, railways

– social development

– repair and maintenance and operation of existing facilities.

3.5.3.   *General*

With the likelihood of falling market share overseas and only small benefits appearing at home, the UK construction industry has to become still more effective in its operation. In examining the competitive situations which are going to be met in the future, it is vital that the natural inclination to reduce spending on research and development is resisted. Well-directed research and development has a major contribution to make towards maintaining and, if possible, improving the industry's market share. Without adequate research and development work, the industry will suffer loss of efficiency below what is already an unsatisfactory level, and it will become increasingly expensive and uncompetitive with consequent discouragement of investment, public or private.

4.   ENERGY SOURCES

4.1.   Introduction

The energy supply industries are characterised by the long time-scales which exist between the decision to develop new technology and its availability for full-scale use. Depending on the nature of the process there is a further extensive time devoted to planning approvals, design, construction and commissioning. Once operating, a power station can stay in place for 30 to 40 years. For these reasons, decisions taken now will affect the security and costs of energy supplies well into the twenty-first .century. The difficulty of predicting demand, fuel prices and public attitudes to different types of generation makes long-term planning extremely difficult. It is important, therefore, to maintain research in a broad range of options for power generation.

From 1981-1985, energy usage in the UK increased by under 3 per cent although Gross Domestic Product rose by nearly 8 per cent in real terms. Even if the economy achieves favourable growth rates in the future, it is likely that efficiency measures will continue to restrict growth in energy demand to a lower level. However, there is a considerable backlog of ageing plant to be replaced, as well as a need to use new investment as a means of creating flexibility between different energy sources.

In 1985/86, coal regained its position as the single most important source of energy, accounting for nearly 36 per cent of total consumption. Coal remains the main source of power generation in the UK, with the industry supplying some 87 m tonnes for this purpose out of a total of 118 m tonnes produced.

The policy of providing a substantial nuclear component may have suffered a set-back as a result of the long drawn out Sizewell Enquiry and the Chernobyl disaster. This could lead to increased interest in alternative sources of energy.

With the exception of hydro-electric and tidal power, renewable energy sources — wind, waves, solar, biomass and geothermal — are in an early state of development and cannot make a major contribution to UK energy supplies in the medium term. However, there appears to be a steady move towards the establishment of a tidal power programme. Other more complex technologies, such as the fast breeder reactor and 'clean' nuclear power through fusion, will hardly appear as practical options for some time to come.

The cross-Channel electricity links with France are an important development. International trading in electrical energy is likely to increase and may lead to more use of pumped storage in the UK as its full potential in system operation terms is developed.

As the offshore oil and gas industry begins to decline in the UK, the challenge is to continue to increase the proportion of British design and construction services and to build a research and development capability that can provide work in the international market.

Energy conservation measures have had a distinct effect in slowing down the growth of demand over the past decade. They are rightly regarded as a means of avoiding the capital and environmental costs of new energy schemes, and of conserving non-renewable resources. Little progress has been made with combined heat and power (CHP) and other developments which utilise waste heat from electricity generation, but they can be expected to contribute to these savings in the future. Allied subjects are the generation of power and the production of methane from domestic and industrial waste.

Many older fossil-fired power stations have been closed in recent years; and, in the medium term, a programme to decommission the Magnox stations will need to be started. The high voltage power grid does not have indefinite life; renewal and uprating is currently in progress and will continue. There is sufficient capacity in the high-pressure gas transmission system, so that no major investment is forseen this century, but some replacement of the 200 000 km of domestic low pressure gas pipeline will be needed.

All energy areas are concerned with reductions of capital and maintenance costs, and improved efficiences of production, transmission and storage. More impartial information on comparative costs under different conditions, taking into account safety and environmental costs, would do much to rationalise the energy debate.

4.2. United Kingdom markets

4.2.1. Nuclear power

Nuclear energy is seen by the Central Electricity Generating Board (CEGB) as the most economical route to electrical power. It is also seen as a means of diversifying sources of energy supply from a concentration on the sensitive areas of coal and oil.

The CEGB would like to construct a small family of perhaps six new stations, each of 1200 MW, before the year 2000, using the pressurised water reactor (PWR) design. These plans are tempered by the awaited Layfield Report, and the need to restore public confidence following the Chernobyl disaster.

The older Magnox stations commissioned in the 1960s will become due for decommissioning by the end of the century. Much work has been done but further research and development is required into their dismantling and into the disposal of the subsequent radioactive waste, for which a programme is already under way.

The areas which will require the greatest attention in the future undoubtedly relate to convincing the public of the safety of nuclear energy. This applies to the reactors themselves, and also to the crucial area of waste disposal. Increased attention will be paid to safety and reliability assessment and quality assurance.

The tendency for the International Atomic Energy Agency (IAEA) and national design requirements to become even more rigorous has led to a deeper consideration of seismic and other safety hazards which has, in turn, led to major research initiatives. Research is also being devoted to the studying of internal and other external hazards and of their dynamic effects on structures.

The programme for the installation of fuel reprocessing plants requires similar attention to safety and reliability. This programme is, however, being questioned on account of the current drop in uranium prices and the environmental debate on waste disposal.

The volume of nuclear waste will continue to grow, whatever decisions are made on the PWR programme. Considerable work is needed to satisfy the public on the adequacy of the proposals. Encapsulation of waste in concrete and the construction and repair of containment vessels involve heavy civil engineering inputs, as does the design of suitable storage sites.

4.2.2.	*Coal*	The recent five-year agreement between British Coal and the CEGB provides for 95 per cent of the Generating Board's coal burn being supplied from British mines. However, strong competitive pressures on the British Coal Industry remain, arising from the recent collapse in oil prices and from low-priced coal supplies from other countries. The industry has responded positively since the miners' dispute, with substantial progress towards establishing a low cost viable industry to meet future market challenges.
4.2.3.	*Fossil fuel power and electricity transmission*	Many older fossil-fuelled power stations have been closed in recent years. Those that remain constitute some 85 per cent of CEGB generating capacity, and consist, in the main, of large high efficiency plant. However, delays in the nuclear power station programme and an increasing electricity demand could lead to the construction of new coal-fired stations. Extension of the life of the existing stations by ten or more years is now considered to be possible, and work on refurbishment will be necessary.

It is expected that the use of oil for electricity generation in the UK will be limited until the early or mid-1990s, when increasing demand will create a need to bring oil-fired plant, presently in reserve, back into service.

Environmental pressure to reduce emissions, particularly to counter acid rain and the 'greenhouse effect', will continue, although public concern has not yet reached the level applied to nuclear power.

Considerable expenditure in the transmission area will also relate to refurbishment. There may also be a move towards greater international trade in electricity, depending on assessment of the cross-Channel link with France.

4.2.4.	*Hydro-electric power*	The UK market for hydro-electric works is inhibited mainly by an absence of sites with suitable hydraulic conditions and by the environmental considerations.

The Dinorwig pumped storage scheme is adequate for present needs, but further pumped storage may be required in the longer term and could warrant investment to meet operational requirements if decisions are made to proceed with nuclear power or with alternative energy sources which produce power out of phase with demand.

4.2.5.	*Alternative energy sources*	Tidal energy appears to be the most immediately promising renewable energy source for UK conditions, with current interest in the Severn, Mersey and other barrages. Under suitable conditions, these could generate electricity at costs comparable with those from coal-fired power stations.

Considerable investigation and development effort is being devoted to a number of possible power station sites. Under suitable conditions, these are now being shown to give a satisfactory return on investment. Such schemes could have spin-off in other areas of interest such as marinas, leisure and navigation. The construction of schemes at several sites having tidal time differences would help to even out lunar-phased generation irregularities.

Wind-produced electricity is economic where diesel generation is used. Forecasts indicate that it will be able to compete with coal, oil and nuclear generation for land-based machines, if hoped for capital cost reductions for production quantities are achieved, with forecast reliability and power availability. Wind electricity generating plant can produce an element of 'firm' power, although the assessment of this is

13

complex, and it is certainly less than that of conventional plants. The shortage of acceptable land sites for quantity production of electricity will limit the investment in the UK over the next two decades.

Wave energy is still in an early development phase, with interests now directed towards foreshore devices rather than large deepwater generators. Opportunities to prove new ideas commercially will be needed.

Solar energy is limited in the UK for climatic reasons, and geothermal energy is likely to be restricted to a few exceptional locations.

All of these alternative energy sources have environmental implications.

4.2.6. *Oil and gas*

Output from the UK North Sea is expected gradually to decline, and future exploration will take place in increasingly difficult climatic and geological conditions, with greater water depths. This exploration is currently cut back, following the fall in world oil prices, but there is a continued search for new methods which will bring marginal fields into commercial development.

The maintenance and safety of existing structures will continue to assume greater importance. Ultimately, as production ceases at some locations, legal requirements for the removal of offshore structures will have to be met. There is an opportunity for the UK to take a world lead in development of techniques and equipment for such removal.

Onshore, the main investment relates to the gradual replacement of 200 000 km of ageing low-pressure distribution pipeline.

4.3. Overseas markets

Thermal and hydro-electric generation, and power transmission continue to be important overseas markets for British industry. They are among the first needs of developing countries. The potential is considerable, and limited only by finance availability. The markets are competitive and the principal development needs are directed towards more economical designs, greater efficiency of operation and ability to utilise local fuels. The UK generating authorities give support in such matters as training, and this is important for maintenance of the existing market position.

In spite of Britain's long-standing position in this field, it is increasingly apparent that the provision of government aid finance is a most important issue if markets are to be held and UK expertise is to be retained. There is a close relationship between British involvement in research and design and British orders for construction work and the supply of mechanical and electrical equipment.

The UK already has some involvement in alternative energy sources. Technical research will open up new markets in these fields. However, with these sources as with nuclear power, until Britian has its own proven and economically viable technology, no significant overseas market can be expected.

4.4. Research needs

Energy production includes a high proportion of process, mechanical and electrical technology. These proposals include general items embracing other technologies but are primarily concerned with those directly affecting the civil engineering industry.

The highest priority items identified in this review are given in italics, but the determination of priorities within this area will occasionally require re-assessment. In the right-hand column, the letters A, N, C, etc. denote the subsections in Section 4.2 to which the items refer. The key is as follows: A – alternative; C – coal; G – gas; H – hydro; N – nuclear; O – offshore; T – thermal; Tr – electricity transmission.

			Energy subsection market area
4.4.1.	*Assembly of physical data*		
		Impact of tidal barrages on sediments	A
		Safety of nuclear waste storage areas with regard to geological hydrological and structural factors	N
		Probabilistic assessment of nuclear risk	N
		Performance of tunnelling systems in mining applications	C
		Factors affecting the take and growth rate of trees and other vegetation used in the restoration of colliery spoil heaps	C
		Monitoring condition of equipment in use to improve reliability and establish preventive maintenance criteria	C
		Comparison of lining specifications and operating results of pressure conduits	H
		Design criteria on vibration/resonance from review of current hydro-electric schemes	H
		Past experience of rock movement in caverns	H
		Environmental/ecological requirements of tidal schemes	A
		Long-term behaviour of soils and foundations subjected to many repetitions of loading	A
		Determination of minimum residual flows to preserve river life downstream of dams	H
		Costing of alternative cooling methods for thermal power stations	T
		Study of the hydraulics of the expansion zone beyond turbines and sluices	A
		Propagation of deep water waves into shallow coastal regions	A
		Wave loading on structures in shallow waters	A
		Measurement of energy from waves in shallow waters	A
		Mechanisms of fatigue failure in steel offshore structures	O
		Performance of drag anchors in varying soil profiles	O
		Further instrumentation of new large offshore structures to monitor safety, design and dynamic performance, and more widespread dissemination of the results	O
4.4.2.	*Materials*	*Long-term properties of concrete for up to one million years*	N
		Resistance to cracking under temperature gradients of concrete mixes	N
		Air tightness of various concrete mixes	N
		Uses for colliery spoil	C
		High strength concretes for shafts and other underground construction	C
		Salt crystallisation damage to underground concrete	C
		Interactions between steel/concrete water passage linings and the rock	H
		Data on fatigue endurance of cast steel	O
4.4.3.	*Design*	*Seismic and impact resistant nuclear designs*	N

Study of alternative nuclear waste management methods and physical design of storage sites	N
Control system for mining equipment to reduce amount of dirt taken with the coal	C
Development of separation, transport and placing systems to retain dirt underground	C
Hopper design: traditional formula inadequate	T
Integrity of cooling tower structures	T
Cheaper transmission tower designs for less demanding overseas locations	Tr
Improved safety of LNG tanks, including bund design and flood safety	G
Reduction of costs for small hydro-schemes by standardisation	H
Designs and construction methods for series production of aerogenerator support structures	A
Design and installation of seabed rock anchors	A
Tensioned riser designs in depths up to 1000 m and pressures up to 10 000 lbf/in²	O
Development of multi-phase flow lines and metering	O
Impact of new heavy lift vessels on offshore structural design	O
Design of systems of single point moorings for deeper water fields	O
Reduction of topsides weight on floating platforms	O
Greater cost effectiveness of subsea production systems	O
Expert systems for offshore structural design and assessment	O

4.4.4.	*Construction*	
	Costing of alternative methods for deep excavations and tunnel linings	H
	New techniques for coal cutting to reduce fines produced, e.g. application of high pressure water	C
	Roof bolting to provide support for underground excavations	C
	Economical alternatives to colliery arches for roadway (tunnel) support	C
	Improved tunnelling/mole equipment	G
	Pre-installed ducts for public utilities	G
	Embankment/dam construction techniques for tidal schemes	A
	Construction methods for barrages, other than caissons	A
	Development of techniques and equipment for removal of large offshore structures, when their use is completed	O
	Equipment and techniques for site investigations in water depths of more than 500 m	O

4.4.5.	*Use*	
	Removal of flue gas pollutants (acid rain) and associated sludge disposal	T
	Methods of removing sulphur from coal before burning (e.g. bacterial)	T
	Improved methods of predicting low pressure gas pipe failure	G

Liquefication/gasification of coal in surface plants	C
Underground gasification of coal	C
Fluidised bed combustion	C
Repair of nuclear waste containment structures without emptying	N
Improved methods of locating gas pipes and detecting leaks	G
Sea bed oil and gas equipment which needs minimum inspection and maintenance	G
Means of countering flora and fauna at water intakes/outfalls	T
Repair methods for tunnels and shafts	H
Coatings to counter marine growth	A
Repair of pipelines at 300 – 1000 m depth	O

4.4.6.	*Other*	*Continued awareness of use of energy efficient materials and methods, uses of waste heat, combined heat and power (CHP) and recycling of waste materials* All
		Further information on the 'greenhouse effect' on world climates over the next century and its relation with CO_2 and other emissions T
		Method of dismantling spent nuclear stations N
		Study of environmental issues impeding hydro-electric schemes H
		Reasons for lack of enthusiasm for private generation under the 1983 act H
		Reduction of visual impact of hydro-electric schemes and aerogenerators H&A

4.5. General research needs

In addition to the research needs set out in section 4.4, this review has identified a number of more general research needs which are given below.

4.5.1. Assembly of physical data

Feed-back of data on actual behaviour of large projects and comparison with design predictions — particularly on vibration/resonance, and environmental effects

Comparison of actual behaviour of hydrodynamic structures with mathematical predictions

Digital mapping of the UK, to include underground services, possibly using on-line optical disc storage

4.5.2. Materials

Improved corrosion resistance of structural steel, including protective coatings for maintenance; effects of fatigue, corrosion fatigue and stress corrosion

Further impartial research on uses of pulverised fuel ash (pfa) and blast furnace slags in concrete, and its variability

Alkali-aggregate reaction, taking into account variability of concrete ingredients; need for rapid tests

Fibre-reinforced concrete development

4.5.3.	*Analysis and design*	More economical foundations, using soil cements, piles, rafts, soil stabilisation
		Software which can be used to transfer British knowledge and methods to the Third World, thereby preserving market influence
		Expert systems which incorporate past experience into design routines in a structured way, and possibly link with comprehensive computer aided design (CAD) systems
4.5.4.	*Construction*	Review of the workings of QA procedures (nuclear experience relevant)
		High pressure jet cutting of rock and concrete
		Integrated computer systems for analysis, design, drawings, bills of quantity, contract management and automated fabrication
		Communications links with sites
4.5.5.	*Use*	Long-term preventative maintenance and repair of concrete especially after sulphate or chloride attack
		Concrete repair methods particularly in difficult environments
		Improved telemetry and remote monitoring
		Electromagnetic survey and pipe leak detection — e.g. from aircraft
		Laser and other electronic security systems for detecting movement, fire, leakages, etc., in nuclear and other installations
		High-density data storage for as-built and maintenance records
		Movement monitoring using optical fibres incorporated in the structure.

5. GROUND ENGINEERING

5.1. State of the market

In common with other aspects of construction, the level of activity in ground engineering is much less than it was in the 1970s.

In the UK, the main motorway programme is nearing completion and there is no requirement in the short term for major new reservoirs. Other Government funded work has been restricted. An indication of the decline in the volume of foundation work is that the size of the piling market is said to have been halved over the past ten years. There are now signs of a slight upturn in construction generally, but whether this will be maintained depends on political and economic factors.

Overseas work for UK firms has also been reduced as a result of an increase in indigenous capability, strong international competition and, more recently, the collapse of the oil price.

The reduced work-load and the correspondingly low profit margins have caused some major contractors to withdraw from site investigation and specialised geotechnical work (piling, grouting, etc.). A further consequence is that new geotechnical processes seldom originate in the UK because profit margins are considered to be inadequate to support R&D work.

In spite of the introduction of BS 5930, concern is still expressed about the failure in many cases to appreciate the importance of high quality site investigation work.

5.2. Recent developments

In spite of the depressed state of the market, progress has been made in recent years in a number of areas of ground engineering.

Techniques of site investigation and in situ testing of soils and rocks have benefited from improved instrumentation (e.g. pressuremeters, piezocone) and from further development of geophysical methods including downhole tests. Progress is being made under the SERC programme in the selection of test sites for the scientific evaluation of such techniques.

Construction techniques now include continuous flight auger piles, reinforced earth and anchor systems, use of geotextiles and geogrids for reinforcement, separation, filtration and drainage, and trenchless installation of pipes and cables.

The rapid growth of more powerful and less costly computers and microprocessors has encouraged the development of further applications of numerical methods, especially finite element methods, in the analysis of multi-dimensional geotechical problems. Microprocessors have also been extensively used for data-logging and analysis of laboratory and in situ tests, and for control of construction processes, e.g. grouting, pile analysers for driven piles and integrity testing of bored piles.

Further use has been made of centrifuge modelling, although it is said that other countries are committing more resources to this technique and hence may soon overtake the UK's leading role.

There is now a better appreciation of the effect of strain on the shear strength of clay soils.

5.3.   Effect of advances in other techniques or disciplines

Reference has been made to the important effect of advances in micro-electronics. Further developments can be expected in computer aided design, instrumentation for in situ and laboratory testing, control of construction processes and monitoring of full-scale performance.

Developments in mechanical and electrical engineering (e.g. robotics) may be applied to construction plant, including tunnelling machines.

Site investigation techniques already involve aspects of geophysics, and this is likely to increase.

New planning concepts and environmental considerations will affect inner city redevelopment, multi-purpose developments overseas and so on.

Some aspects of biology and chemistry are relevant to problems of land reclamation and development.

5.4.   Probable areas of future demand

Market areas which are likely to be of continuing or increasing importance include:

- underground storage for nuclear waste and for other hazardous or contaminating materials
- highly mechanised underground mines with larger diameter, deeper shafts
- tunnels, for transportation and for infrastructure renewal
- building on poor ground, including reclaimed, contaminated and undermined land
- seabed works for oil, gas and mineral extraction
- redevelopment of inner city areas and old industrial sites
- inspection and maintenance of existing works, e.g. earth retaining structures, embankment dams, flood defences and main drainage
- new and improved geotechnical processes and construction techniques.

5.5.   R&D needs in ground engineering

The number of topics in which there is a need for research is large and only a few of these can be mentioned here.

There is a continuing need for improved methods of site investigation, including recovery and testing of high quality (i.e. undisturbed) samples of soils and rocks, and further development of in situ tests.

Further investigation of materials on the seabed, from both continental shelf and deep ocean areas, and of calcareous sands and non-sedimentary soils from non-temperate regions is required.

More work is necessary on the description, classification and characterisation of rock masses in terms useful for engineering analysis and design.

More information is required on the behaviour of soils and rocks when subjected to cyclic and dynamic (including seismic) loading to extremes of temperature.

The design of foundations and earth structures to withstand dynamic loading also deserves further study.

For safe and economical design of foundations (including piled foundations), earth retaining structures (conventional and reinforced earth), tunnels and other underground structures, it is necessary to take into account ground/structure interaction. Improved mathematical methods of analysing such problems are being developed but these must be verified by monitoring full-scale structures. Similarly, theoretical predictions of deformations in embankment dams, open pit mines, etc., should be checked against full-scale observations to confirm or refine the theories used.

In the UK, it is increasingly important to make good use of poor ground, including reclaimed land, old industrial sites, etc. Research needs relating to problems in water supply and drainage in land reclamation are discussed in Chapter 10, Section 10.8. Various techniques for ground improvement have been developed to improve bearing capacity and to reduce structural settlement. Further work is desirable to determine the efficiency of such techniques in various soil conditions.

The use of geotextiles has increased in recent years. Here there is a need for further research into the behaviour of geotextiles and geogrids in association with soils rather than 'in-isolation' material tests.

It is important that a sensible balance should be maintained in all future ground engineering research work. Fundamental work should continue in order to obtain improved knowledge of the constitutive relationships of soils and rocks and to apply the latest computational techniques in design. However, at the present stage of development, greater benefits are likely to accrue from properly designed large-scale works during and after construction. Such work will require substantial resources and close collaboration between research workers, consultants and contractors.

5.6.   List of R&D topics in ground engineering

This list is based on recommendations contained in the specialist papers of Volume 3. The reference numbers of the relevant Task Force papers are given in parentheses with the letter C denoting a recent review paper.

The highest priority items identified in this review are given in italics, but the determination of priorities within this area will occasionally require re-assessment.

5.6.1.   Assembly of physical data

New approaches to inner city reclamation and development (P24)

Lessons from recent overseas developments (especially multi-purpose) (P24)

Establishment of a UK seismic network and determination of design ground motions appropriate to local soil conditions (D10, D22C)

Improved site investigation techniques including geophysical and other methods of in situ testing for relevant properties of soils and rocks, including landfill and seabed materials (P15, P16C, P18C, P24C, P30, D10, D11)

Methods of locating defects in embankment dams, cavities and underground services (P5C, P16C, P30, D11)

Improvement of remote control methods of monitoring deformation, strain, pressure and force both during and after construction, including measurements in retaining walls, tunnels, slopes, rock fill and earth dams (P5, P15, P16, P30, D10, D11)

Determination of in situ stresses in rocks (D10)

Description and characterisation of rock masses in terms (including probabilistic ones) useful in engineering design (D10)

Studies of environmental effects of major civil engineering projects (P5, P15, P24)

5.6.2.   *Materials*   Disposal or useful adaptation of waste materials (P24)

Durability of concrete and other materials in contact with deleterious substances (P24)

Spontaneous combustion of fill materials (P24)

Properties of soils and rocks under cyclic and dynamic loading (P20, D22)

Properties of soils and rocks subjected to extreme temperatures (D10, D11)

Properties of soils (especially overseas) relating mode of origin to engineering behaviour) (D10, D11)

Performance of geotextiles and geogrids in various soils

5.6.3.   *Analysis and design*   *Finite element analysis to predict strains in embankment dams and opencast mines (P5, P15)*

Stability of rock-fill control dams to through or overtopping flow (P5)

Behaviour of lagoon deposits and tailings dams under rapid loading (P24C)

Movement of contaminants, including spillage from cryogenic storage, through ground and consequent changes in soil characteristics (P24, P24C, D11)

Design methods taking into account ground/structure interaction (including pile groups, support systems for underground excavations, and reinforced earth) (P16, P16C, P30, D11)

Effect of earthquake and blast loading on structures above and below ground and on dams (P5, P30, D22)

Prediction of shock and vibration transmission through soil and rock, arising from blasting, piling, compaction and other construction activities (P15, P16C, P30)

Long-term stability of tunnels and storage caverns, including the effects and behaviour of ground water (P16C, P24, P30 D10)

Design of deep cuttings and open cut mines with regard to face stability (P15, P15C, D10)

Design of foundations on the seabed, including tension piles, anchorage and slope stability assessment (P18C, D11)

Problems in soil dynamics (foundation competence, slope stability, liquefaction potential and prevention) (D22)

Relationship between structural response, and damage, and ground motion due to earthquakes (D22)

Study of permanent displacements of foundations, slopes and dams arising from seismic loading (D22)

Study of new uses of underground space (P16)

Problems associated with underground development of oil shales and gasification of coal (P24)

5.6.4.   *Construction*   Control of ground water during construction of open cut mines, tunnels and underground structures (P15C, P16, P30, D10)

Improvements in linings of tunnels and shafts with better methods of sealing (P16, P30)

Drilling large diameter and deep shafts, including ground treatment in permeable strata (P16, D10)

22

Improved techniques for tunnelling in non-cohesive soils and in variable ground (P16, D10)

Techniques producing tunnels in rock more economically and with reduced roughness (P30)

Improved methods of rock breaking and removal especially at great depth and under water (P15, P16, P30)

Pollution control (dust, noise, vibration, etc.) (P15)

Improved methods of spoil transport and continuous reclamation (pneumatic, hydraulic and conveyor belt systems), including effects of abrasion and stickiness of transported material (P15, P15C, P16, P24)

Design and construction of haul and other temporary roads (P15)

Comparison of ripping and blasting operations in open pit mines (P15C)

Development of seabed excavation and trenching techniques (P18C, D11)

Drainage techniques for reclaimed land and for stabilisation of landslides (horizontal and vertical drains and application of vacuum) (P24, D11)

Development of geotechnical processes (freezing, grouting with predictable penetration and effectiveness, effectiveness of dynamic compaction and of lime columns in weak soils and fill) (P16, P24, P24C, D10, D11)

Problems of hydrofracture, controlled directional fracturing in rock and flow of fluids in fractured rocks (D10)

Storage and handling of topsoil (P24)

Stabilisation and improvement of land for cultivation (P24C)

5.6.5. *Use*

Internal erosion of embankment dams (P5C, D11)

Reservoir sedimentation and decommissioning of silt filled reservoirs (P5C, P24)

Assessment of old underground structures (P30)

Methods of renewing and renovating tunnels in service (P30)

Techniques for removal of offshore structures and pipelines after decommissioning (P18C, P20C)

Studies of damage due to ground movement, including effects of traffic vibration, adjacent construction, mineral extraction, trees, landslides and creep of clay slopes (D11, D11C)

Resistance of grassed slopes to erosion from flood flow (P5C)

6.   STRUCTURAL ENGINEERING

6.1.   State of the market

6.1.1.   *State of the market in the UK*

Progress in the building industry will always be disturbed by changes in fiscal measures and political philosophies: an example of a development arising from these is the London Docklands. Another example is the policy exercised by Government departments and nationalised industries to dispose of surplus property and land, freeing them for development. Changed rules permitting the construction without specific authority for non-conventional building is leaving the way open for management or turnkey contracts for health buildings.

In some cases, accelerated building processes have given rise to more speedy building. Some of the changes are managerial but others include an increased amount of pre-fabrication brought about by the need to depart from the labour-intensive practices of the past.

Refurbishment is now seen as an important growth area — and is, incidentally, the subject of an increasing number of publications at the professional institutions. Under Government direction, the scene is now set for the sale by local authorities of 'hard to let' estates for major refurbishment and sale, at low selling levels, into the private sector.

With lower prices and reduced profits, it is thought that the oil industry will be less willing than in the past to commit funds for the reduction of environmental pollution. However, safety and 'reliability engineering' will assume increasing importance.

The development of privatised telecommunications networks and also of cellular networks has resulted in an increase in business in the last two years. The demand is expected to continue for the next year or so, after which it will fall back to its former level.

The major advances in computing and information technology have made the handling and transmission of data easier. These have, in general, been matched by significant progress in the instrumentation in data gathering.

6.1.2.   *State of the market overseas*

With the fall-off in oil revenues, energy-rich non-industrial countries may turn even more towards traditional low-energy construction, although there will always be the tendency to copy Western solutions for prestige purposes.

With the economic changes in these countries, it is possible that there may be a market for the provision of plots with services only; buildings would be provided by the occupier. Particularly in the offshore industry, the UK should plan strategically to use experience gained in the North Sea as a foundation for selling engineering expertise world-wide when a downturn occurs in home-based requirements. The adoption of an unnecessarily protectionist stand could be counter-productive in the long term.

Communications and broadcasting are high on the political priority list even before the more basic infrastructure needs have been satisfied. Schemes which go ahead are usually controlled by financial considerations — either by grants or long-term loans from national or international agencies or, to a lesser extent, by oil revenues.

The use of solar energy to drive radio and microwave projects can have a significant effect on the size of structures which hitherto were required only to support the aerials. Solar generators in themselves lead to a demand for structures but, increasingly, these are simply supports.

| 6.2. | Rate of deterioration/improvement |

Although alternative feedstocks to natural hydrocarbons will be required in the long term, it is evident that crude shortages as viewed in 1981 were a short-term artificial condition; feedstock availability is not now liable to be a constraint in the short/medium term.

In 1981, it was considered that small planning systems suitable for engineering operations, making use of desk top type machines, would be increasingly common, and that engineering training should put more emphasis on these activities. This is still considered to be valid and is supported by the considerable progress in the availability of hardware and software, as well as in CAD/CAM and Information Systems.

Progress is being made with new automatic welding processes, particularly for submarine pipeline constructions. The capacity of heavy-lift vessels has made significant advances and the adoption of semi-submersible hull forms for construction vessels has improved operability.

Within the broadcasting and telecommunication fields, it has been found difficult to foresee areas of growth. With the high degree of coverage at present achieved in both these areas, work is only likely to develop from the modernisation of existing systems brought about by the introduction of new technology. This work will not compensate for the developments of previous years and a smaller home market is forecast for the future.

The report on progress in the field of thermal power stations considers that there has been very little if any progress concerning the problem areas identified in the original report.

| 6.3. | Future needs relating to areas of most concern |

Although in the health building programme there has been an increase in activity as a result of the sale of surplus property and estates, there persists the problem of finding suitable new sites. In urban areas these remain less than ideal.

Inadequate vapour checking in past construction has been of great concern; this is becoming increasingly important and will justify relevant research.

The emergence of new materials and processes has brought with it many benefits and many problems. Much research is required into the manufacture, methods of application, maintenance, durability and repair of these materials. The relationships between accelerated testing in the laboratory and performance in practice is thought to justify careful analysis. Easy and practical methods, by which a non-specialist may test materials and elements, merit a high priority.

A particular area to which urgent attention should be given is the corrosion of pre-stressed concrete tendons, a process which may be far more prevalent than was previously supposed. The implication of this for important structures is clear.

In the field of radio and telecommunications structures, the problems of aerodynamically forced vibrations have not yet been resolved and it may well be that the vibrations caused by aerodynamic/mechanical influences (such as with wind generators) may create more severe problems. Existing work being done by CIRIA and others should be extended. A plea is made also for more facilities for full-scale testing of masts and towers; these structures are almost alone in civil engineering in requiring full-scale testing for validation.

6.4. Effects of recent innovations and advances in other technologies

The most obvious source of influences upon structural engineering from other technologies is energy and its management. The advent of low energy buildings brings with it consequences for the foundations and superstructure of affected buildings.

These buildings are frequently required not only to be energy-efficient but also to accommodate high-technology processes. Almost complete freedom from transmitted vibrations is a common requirement; very close working tolerances and small differential settlements are others.

For microwave and telecommunications structures, dimensional and rotational stability is vital.

Chemical technology has produced a number of effects — both direct and indirect. Work on resins is likely to have increasing significance in the future, whether for use as adhesives between steel and concrete (it is already well established in bridges but less well so for post-hoc reinforcement of concrete slabs) and timber structures, or as coatings. Coated reinforcement is assuming an increasing significance in the USA as a means of protecting the steel from corrosion caused by the action of de-icing salts; it is possible that existing research work may lead to its wider adoption in the UK. The application of resin and other plastic coatings to steel in large panels is already widespread and increasing, with the benefits of relative freedom from maintenance requirements making it most attractive in claddings and especially in inaccessible locations — e.g. the undersides of bridges whether as protection or to facilitate maintenance access.

The increasing use of pulverised fuel ash (pfa) in concrete brings with it certain advantages such as workability, reduced heat generation and the use of a material that might otherwise be wasted. Certain disadvantages include a reduced rate of gain of strength, a need for a more strict control on curing especially with the sections, and a limited amount of experience of its long-term behaviour, especially when used in combination with other than traditional materials or with other 'grey powders'. Other water-reducing agents are likely to be used, and more needs to be known about their long-term performance.

Silica fume, not yet in general use as a concreting admixture in the UK, is likely to be employed to an increasing extent; the health implications will need to be explored, as will its durability.

As is the case in all other fields of engineering, microprocessors are having an ever-growing influence in the field of structural engineering. They have a particularly important input on non-destructive testing for the nuclear power industry, but the full potential for metal manufacture and advanced manufacturing generally has still to be realised. In instrumentation, 'intelligent' multi-channel data loggers are now available.

Satellite images permit easier prospecting and other forms of survey. Acoustic emission monitoring can detect cracks very efficiently.

6.5. Dynamics of structures

The subject of structural dynamics, not included in the 1981 Report, has implications for the whole range of structural engineering. Engineers need training to be able to carry out dynamic analysis and to identify and remedy dynamic problems.

The sources of the vibration are many; the structures which may be affected by them are even more numerous. Methods do exist for carrying out such analysis but faster and more efficient ones are needed. Improvements in computers will help, accompanied by the development of a data bank of vibration data.

Dynamic testing procedures and equipment are under continuous development and several firms already specialise in dynamic testing. Data are needed on the stiffness and damping characteristics of soils.

It is possible that more research is needed into the human reaction of dynamic response, and the results could be incorporated in design guides or codes of practice.

Undergraduates in universities and polytechnics do not usually have an adequate grounding in structural dynamics; in most cases, it is insufficient for competent design or for communicating with specialists.

The formulation of a research programme could be put in the hands of a working group or explored at a conference.

While much of the material in the immediately preceding paragraphs relates to dynamics generally, a strong plea is made for attention to the particular requirements of earthquake engineering.

6.6. Management

The review also identified the need for more relevant research and technology transfer in the field of management. Little has been done to implement the recommendations of the Task Force Report in this respect. The SERC 'specially promoted programme' on management was geared too much to the production of higher degrees; a new approach here could be beneficial.

6.7. R&D needs in structural engineering

The high priority items identified in this review are given in italics, but the determination of priorities within this area will occasionally require re-assessment.

6.7.1. Assembly of physical data

In earthquake engineering, the assessment of hazard and the definition of the design ground motions (dynamic loads) appropriate to given geographical regions and local soil conditions

Input loading and shear strength properties of foundation and materials under seismic loading

Dynamic methods in earthquake engineering, e.g. shear wave velocities, dynamic response tests and laboratory soil tests

Ground accelerations during earthquakes have been found to be larger than previously thought; structures *not* designed to resist earthquakes have survived! New data would rationalise design.

It is for consideration that there should be a UK seismic network under a single national organisation. The network, which would also be equipped with strong-motion portable accelerographs, would record earthquakes and publish precise information about them. It is likely that this information would be channelled not only through the Institute of Geological Sciences (IGS) but also through universities and other institutions concerned with nuclear and offshore programmes.

In the field of offshore engineering, considerably more work is required to establish realistic design criteria relating to drift and the dynamic effect of wind turbulence.

The detection of load variations and deterioration in structures by examining responses to known or random vibrations

Development of methods of determining wave loading in shallow water

6.7.2. *Materials*

Definition of limits on composition of cement and aggregates for the control of alkali-aggregate reaction

Field studies on the effect of admixtures and additives, including blended cements, on durability

Effect of curing of concrete on carbonation and relationship between carbonation and corrosion of steel

Effect of aggressive agents on steel and concrete in actual structures

Effect of different aggregates, additives and admixtures on the hydration of cement

Quantitative methods of appraisal of concrete in situ and the assessment of deterioration

Conservation of energy and resources: further applications of dense and lightweight aggregates from waste materials, including economic appraisal of their use

Performance of alkali-resistant fibres in concrete structures

Performance of concrete under extremes of stress, temperature and hydraulic pressure

Review of other possible applications of concrete in the engineering industry generally, e.g. machine tools

Design data on fatigue endurance of cast steel

Fire resistance of concrete construction with artificial aggregates

Refined methods for identifying materials, their properties and their stresses or strains (without stress-relieving)

Relationship between masonry unit strength, mortar strength and masonry strength

Development of standard tests for strength and properties other than durability and weather exclusion

Non-destructive test methods for masonry

Improved higher strength steels are being used but new problems continue to appear; further work is needed.

Properties and reliability of mooring materials, particularly for man-made fibres

The use of copper for roofing is growing in Europe but it is not popular in the UK. If properly installed, however, it provides excellent roofing material and may be worth examining.

Cathodic protection systems

6.7.3. *Analysis and design (including complete structures)*

Performance under high-cycle (over 10^8) variable amplitude loading, under various environmental conditions of complete wind turbine components; likely materials are welded low alloy steel, fibre composites and laminated wood

Rationalisation of safety in design: acquisition of data on relevant parameters and their variability to design for safety and serviceability with some applications to the simplification of design procedures

Appraisal for acceptable levels of risk

Design for thermal loading

Software based upon minimisation methods for vibrations, making use of the super computer

Fatigue related to different joint geometries/ring stiffened joints; although

there have been significant advances, the mechanism of fatigue failure in steel offshore structures is still a long way from being understood; more work is needed.

Tension piles; work is still required where stress reversals (tension/compression) occur.

The development of reliable design methods for piles in calcareous soils

Realistic design factors for the calculation of the ultimate load capacity of piles

For single point moorings, development is needed to produce systems for the deeper water fields which may be discovered in the future.

Full-scale type testing on transmission line towers and similar structures of very light section

Development of easily usable methods of test of all kinds of buildings and elements; this work would be required for the benefit of both professional and technician engineers.

Development of optimum design, construction methods and plant for the series production of support structures of offshore wind turbine generators

Development of methods of determining the effect of breaking waves on flexible structures

Determination of long-term behaviour in a marine atmosphere of conventional materials with or without protective coatings under cyclic loading

Although some research is in progress into limit state design methods for connections in steel and concrete buildings and bridges, there is little or no research into bearings and fixings, and this would be worthwhile.

6.7.4.	*Construction (including decommissioning and demolition)*

Durability and repair of concrete; methods of ensuring that key aspects of control are identified and that the levels of control required are reached on actual structures

Methods of demolition of concrete structures

Research is needed in view of the increasing interest in the combined use of castings, forgings and wrought metal products joined by welding.

Development of high frequency induction welding (although some work in modelling welding processes is in progress)

Corrosion of pre-stressing tendons; this is assuming increasing significance

Tendering and contract procedures: investigation of design team organisation and two-stage tendering procedures to involve the general contractor in the development of the final design

As offshore installations are decommissioned, their partial or total removal becomes necessary. The development of techniques and equipment for carrying out the removal of large offshore structures is an area where further work is necessary; this is an opportunity for the UK to take the lead.

The demolition of major structures — and particularly thermal power stations — is a very sensitive matter. There is merit in examining ways of ensuring that demolition contractors are in possession of relevant information and adequately worked out procedures (including dealing with fragile structures and with dangerous materials such as asbestos).

6.7.5. *Use*

The repair, repairability and reinstatement of structures; the advent of new materials and the enforced use of materials known to have certain undesirable characteristics make it increasingly important to have techniques available for carrying out repairs of adequate durability.

Each new structure is a prototype; for a relatively minute expenditure, it would be possible to instrument the more relevant structures (including offshore structures) and thus learn a great deal. An investigation should be instigated into ways of ensuring that this information is not lost but is collated, interpreted, publicised and made use of in future design. It is likely that this is one of the most cost-effective design proposals in the whole exercise. Procedures for establishing data banks are more generally available now than ever before.

For offshore structures, improved jacket repair techniques

6.7.6. *Research needs which do not fit into market sectors*

Avoidance of inadvertent over-stretching of existing technology

Examination of the overall value-for-money of recent changes in building legislation

There is a lack of adequate exchange of knowledge between the various members of the construction industry and professions. There is evidence of insufficient co-ordination between the construction research and information services (research institutes, universities, industry, Government departments). There is a lack of readily available, reliable, up-to-date information on hazard assessment. Engineers and other design professionals are not given adequate practical training in universities in safety matters, quality assurance, dynamic and certain other realistic aspects of the behaviour of structures. A research study should be established to examine these problems and to report.

As an extension of the preceding item, there is a need for a widely acceptable but not alarmist early warning system of possible problems.

The role and status of the engineer have been the subject of much debate. Changed and changing procedures initiated by Government departments and nationalised industries will have far-reaching consequences, not all of which have yet been understood. It is likely that they will extend into overseas engagements, not always to the advantage of the UK. It is considered that a study to examine these changes should be initiated.

In the last decade, certain sectors of the construction industry have experienced a fall in productivity. This is claimed to have resulted from changes in site industrial relations procedures. In some instances there have been significant rises in costs. Most recently, the CEGB has taken a number of initiatives which are claimed to have brought about improvements. A study of the changes and the claimed improvements is merited.

7.   BUILDING

7.1. Introduction	Most, possibly all, civil engineers will at some time in their careers have responsibility for building work. For many, building work in all its aspects will be their principal activity. This has always been true but in recent years the moves away from traditional materials have introduced technological problems whose solution has necessitated an understanding of technology that fits well within a civil engineer's training. It is for this reason that the present paragraphs are included in the report.

It would be inappropriate for civil engineers to make a bid to do work which is more properly the responsibility of architects, building surveyors or other construction professionals; it is reasonable, however, to assume that a study of the research needs of building is of concern to civil engineers.

Bearing in mind the importance of building in the totality of construction, there is a strong need for a major review of R&D requirements in building, involving a high degree of co-operation and participation by research workers and practitioners in this field. The EDC Research Strategy Committee Report draws attention to some of the high priority R&D areas in building.

In these circumstances, this Report can only emphasise the need for a more extensive and effective building R&D programme, and offer the following outline proposals that are derived from consultation meetings with representatives of most of the leading professional construction institutions, as well as of CIRIA and the Building Research Establishment (BRE) concerned with construction.

During the consultations, it has become clear that the nature of the research required is at a 'high level' rather than at a merely 'nuts and bolts level'. In looking ahead over a substantial period, changes which are likely to affect buildings and hence building research should be outlined as a context in which research requirements are defined.

7.2.   Proposals

7.2.1. Technology transfer	Much valuable research work and much information as feedback from practical construction never gets transferred to practitioners. Equally, and not infrequently, the transfer of information from the designer into construction is inefficient. The valuable information sheets and reports issued by BRE, CIOB and CIRIA are examples of practical elements of technical education; but they are not always as well known as they should be. The highest possible priority should be given to research into the best devices for making technology transfer take place efficiently.
7.2.2. Interfaces between the professions	Advances in the technology of new materials and processes have outstripped the understanding of many craftsmen. Designers — in whatever profession — have not always realised the extent to which these changes have affected their own particular contribution to the overall design of buildings: many of these changes are, indeed, the result of work by scientists and technologists remote from the construction professions.

Examples of these are all aspects of jointing and connections; others include behaviour of structures in fire, the durability of wall-ties, the design of claddings, wind around buildings and fixings (security, techniques, loads, materials). Research is required to examine the interfaces — and gaps — between the professions and to produce recommendations with the aim of ensuring that critical matters are not left unattended by default.

7.2.3. *Whole system*

At present, each professional, in contributing to the design of a building, deals with matters within his own specialism. The designer with overall responsibility, most frequently but not invariably the architect, will ensure that the whole building comes together to meet the client's requirement. It is seldom possible, however, for him to know for certain how the building interacts with its environment, how the services and building interact, how design relates to maintenance and services to fabric. The interaction between professions, and between the professions and the clients, is important to understand but is not, at first sight, an obvious candidate to be a research project. The solution is likely to be that all related research items should bear these matters in mind, consciously.

7.3. Conclusion

Towards the conclusion of the consultation, it became apparent that an initiative already being pursued by some construction institutions held out some hope for the enlargement of research in building. The impending establishment of the Construction Research Board will no doubt affect this, but the co-operation of the Institution in these developments would offer the prospect of a means of accommodating the particular research requirements, in building, of civil engineers.

8. MARITIME ENGINEERING

8.1. Introduction

Maritime engineering is broadly defined as comprising all engineering carried out in the tidal environment, thus including civil engineering related to estuaries, coastlines and offshore structures. In practice, this is not a homogeneously integrated branch of civil engineering, and is subdivided into better recognised specialities such as navigation and dredging, port engineering, coast protection and offshore engineering. There are overlapping interests between the specialities — e.g. offshore engineering, coast protection and port engineering all have an interest in research into the prediction of offshore wave climate, albeit for use in different ways. However, they all have different needs and priorities, and it is unrealistic to regard this as one single category of civil engineering within which research priorities can generally be agreed and defined. The needs of each sector, as listed in Section 8.3, stand justified in their own right, and they cannot and should not be set against the priorities of other unrelated areas of activity within maritime engineering.

An independent and thorough review of research requirements in coastal engineering has recently been completed by the Coastal Engineering Research Panel appointed by the Maritime Engineering Group Board of the Institution of Civil Engineers (Reference: Research Requirements in Coastal Engineering. The Institution of Civil Engineers, February 1985). Coastal engineering was defined as that branch of civil engineering concerned with the planning, design and construction of works related to the coastal environment and its enhancement, embracing shoreline protection, navigation channels and harbours, industrial intakes and outfalls, submarine pipelines and offshore mineral extraction. National research needs and priorities for future attention were explored and defined in detail by working parties covering three general subject areas:

- beaches and sea walls

- dredging and dispersion

- coastal harbours, breakwaters and offshore islands.

The work of the Coastal Engineering Research Panel within these subject areas has been more fundamental and thorough than that carried out by the ICE Research Sub-Committee. Therefore, although research needs in these areas have been included within this maritime engineering review, the report of the Coastal Engineering Research Panel is recommended as being a more expansive and definitive statement for the subject areas within its remit.

8.2. Market prospects and trends

8.2.1. Sea defences

Defending the coast from erosion and flooding by the sea is an outstanding example of civil engineering construction where failure to carry out improvement works can result in capital expenditure which far outweighs the cost of preventive works. About 2000 lives were lost during the North Sea floods of 1953, and in the UK about £25 million (at 1953 prices) had to be spent on immediate restoration and improvement works. Since that time, there have been frequent inundations and flood damage around the coast — for example, at Teignmouth in 1975, Ilfracombe in 1978, Torcross in 1979 and Morecambe in 1977 and 1983. While erosion is not so spectacular or dangerous, property swallowed by the sea is an asset lost forever.

The capital and maintenance costs of coast protection and sea defence in the UK are very high, of the order of £50 million per annum at present. The replacement value of existing works is at least £4 billion. Nevertheless, the design of these works continues, to a large extent, to be based on experience; it is one of the most difficult but least codified branches of civil engineering. Research is leading the trend towards more natural and cost-effective means of providing coast protection.

Unit costs of coast protection works vary considerably according to the problems of particular locations and the different classes of protection. The Coastal Engineering Research Panel has suggested the following order of costs:

Cliff protection, grading and drainage, with sea walls, groynes and beach replacement	£5000 per metre
Sea walls, offshore barriers or sea embankments	£2000 – £4000 per metre
Beach replenishment (periodically recurrent)	£350 – £900 per metre
Simple revetments and breakwork	£200 – £4000 per metre

Because failure could result in considerable financial loss, the incentive for designers to seek innovative and possibly less costly schemes is restricted by the present limited state of knowledge. Investment in research is justified not only by improved design techniques but also by the much greater saving that could be achieved if the research ensured that the right protection scheme for the location were chosen, thus eliminating the expense of further remedial measures within its lifetime.

8.2.2. Sedimentation and dredging

A thorough understanding of the process by which sediments of all kinds are transported in the tidal marine environment is essential for the efficient design of navigation channels and port facilities so as to minimise the quantity of dredging necessary. It is also a necessary input to the optimisation of dredging and disposal of dredged sediments, which is a costly maintenance expenditure in many ports.

The annual cost of maintenance dredging for channels and harbour basins in the UK is of the order of £25 million (Coastal Engineering Research Panel, 1985). Dredging and disposal costs can be apportioned thus:

Load into dredge hopper
25p – 50p per m^3 (according to type of material)

Transport to offshore discharging ground
1·5p – 4·0p per m^3/km

If, as a result of research, relocated spoil grounds could reduce the distance travelled by the dredger on the round trip, considerable savings could be made. For example, the annual quantity dredged from the East Coast ports is about 12 million m^3; if the average distance to dump could be shortened, the cost saving would be around £270 000 per annum, per kilometre reduction.

Turnover in offshore dredging to win sand and gravel is currently about £60 million per annum. If larger areas of the sea bed could be licensed for extraction, pressure on land based resources would be relieved. Large deposits are at present unworkable owing to lack of research into nearshore patterns of sediment transport and wave climate. There is no doubt that a clearer picture of the effects of dredging, with better understanding of possible alternative measures, would bring considerable benefits.

Research into problems of sediment scour should give two types of benefit. Firstly, the cost of maintaining coastal structures such as sea walls could be substantially reduced. Secondly, there would be great financial benefits if the scour process could be controlled, so that pipelines buried themselves in the sea bed without the need for trenching. The cost saving, if self-scouring and burial could be achieved, has been estimated at about £50 000 per kilometre of pipeline. To set the scale of potential savings, it has been estimated that in the next ten years about 2000 kilometres of pipeline will be laid in the UK sector of the North Sea alone.

| 8.2.3. | *Dispersion of discharge* | The discharge of dredged estuarine sediments into marine waters is currently an active environmental issue that threatens the viability of many British Ports, particularly on the seaboard of the North Sea. A clear, quantifiable understanding of the dispersion and ultimate destination of discharged dredged sediments, and their impact (if any) on the marine environment, is urgently required to defend the UK port industry against unreasonable restrictions implying uneconomically high operating costs. |

The discharge of effluents into coastal waters is also a cause of considerable concern for environmental reasons; there are strong political pressures to stop coastal discharges. It has been estimated that the alternative method of disposal on land would cost an extra £90 million per annum in the UK. Research aimed at improving the performance of outfall diffusers and at predicting the dispersal of pollutants must, therefore, be beneficial for environmental, financial and political reasons.

In power station design, cooling water temperature is critically important — overheating could cause station shut down at a cost of about £600 000 per day. Locating the intake so far away from the outfall as to eliminate recirculation of warm water can, however, be expensive; intake tunnels usually cost about £5000 per metre. If, for example, an intake tunnel could be shortened by 100 m as a result of research into outfall dispersion and the stability of thermal plumes, there would be a saving of about £500 000.

For these reasons, continued development and refinement of predictive modelling of the dispersion of discharges into tidal waters will provide a high return in both financial and environmental terms.

| 8.2.4. | *Docks, harbours and maritime works* | The design and construction of coastal harbours and breakwaters are a major source of invisible earnings overseas by British consulting engineers and contractors. For example, in 1982, the relevant figures were: |

<blockquote>

Capital value of overseas works on docks and
　　harbours by British consultants　　　　　　　　　　£700 million

Value of maritime works overseas completed
　　by British contractors　　　　　　　　　　　　　　£180 million

Contribution to the balance of payments　　　　　　　£65 million

</blockquote>

In order to maintain this record, in the face of ever-increasing international competition, it is essential that designers should benefit from the results of continuing research into ship motions and handling, harbour configuration and breakwaters. For example, although designs in most branches of civil engineering can be completed to a high level of confidence, this is by no means the case for breakwaters. Reported failures of an unacceptably large number of breakwaters during the last seven years have demonstrated large gaps in present knowledge. It has been estimated that the present cost of damage to existing breakwaters, world-wide, is of the order of £250 million. A major research effort to improve the situation is long overdue and there is the opportunity for Britain to take the lead in breakwater design.

Contractors would obtain corresponding benefits. The construction of maritime works, often in a hostile environment, is subject to greater uncertainties, hazards and risk than most other types of construction. At the tender stage, contractors need a better assessment of the circumstances of construction, and during construction, a better basis for determining changes of method which take into account changed circumstances. Knowledge based on research is essential if UK civil engineers are to be competitive in the overseas market and to benefit UK manufacturing industry.

8.2.5. Offshore engineering

Recent forecasting by the Scottish Development Agency indicates that expenditure in the UK Continental Shelf, which is primarily the North Sea, will total about £20 billion over the next decade, even if an oil price (in real terms) of US$15 per barrel prevails. If the price averages US$21, the expenditure is predicted to be about £34 billion during the same period.

The future development of UK fields is likely to be on fields with less than 100 million barrels of recoverable reserves. To maintain production beyond the year 2000, some 86 small fields are likely to be developed, as compared with the 28 currently approved fields which are at present producing or are under development. Although deeper water areas with prospects exist to depths of up to 400 m in Norway and in northern waters, the main activity is expected to be confined to water depths of 100-250 m, and it is unlikely that there will be interest in research directed towards the hydrocarbon deposits that are more expensive to exploit. The prospect of lower oil prices places greater emphasis on research that could lead to more economical and cost-effective designs.

8.2.6. Overseas earnings

At the end of 1984, the Association of Consulting Engineers estimated that its members were responsible for about £2400 million worth of maritime works under construction world-wide, including harbours, navigation channels, sea walls, etc. Overseas earnings from coastal engineering have been estimated at about £65 million in 1983; the overseas earnings of British contractors over the years has been comparable with those of consultants.

Recent years have seen increasing international competition in a diminishing market. The UK civil engineering industry has a highly respected record of expertise and achievement in port and coastal engineering. It now also has a well-established UK offshore engineering experience which provides the potential to export technology and services into other offshore areas such as North America, South-East Asia and the Far East.

In today's fiercely competitive international markets, in which some overseas competitors attempt to temper lower technical ability or experience by means of attractive financial packages, designers and builders need a continuous research back-up so that technical excellence is maintained in a period of rapid change. The UK maritime civil engineering industry will continue to maintain its contribution to the balance of payments only if its expertise and reputation are fostered by high-grade, well-directed and well co-ordinated research.

8.3.   Research needs

The following summaries of research topics are drawn from the recommendations of the 1981 Task Force, with comments, amendments and additional suggestions by the members of the ICE Maritime Engineering Board and the reviewers of the original Task Force papers. They should not be regarded as an absolutely definitive and complete statement of research needs; in particular, the Report, 'Research Requirements in Coastal Engineering', of the Coastal Engineering Research Panel, supplements and expands these summaries in the subject areas of beaches and sea walls, dredging and dispersion, and coastal harbours, breakwaters and offshore islands.

The comments in brackets identify progress or changes since 1981, and highlight specific problems or specific needs. It is not possible to assign priorities between the subject areas, but topics of highest importance within each subject are given in italics.

8.3.1.   Coastal works

State-of-the-art study to provide guidelines of good practice in coast protection (some specific guidelines produced, such as, for example, more wave walls needed; feedback from experience required)

Development of more orderly and effective methods of evaluating and approving coastal works (little progress; requires co-ordination of public bodies, and acceptable method of calculating cost effectiveness. Urgent)

Review and development of conceptual/mathematical models suitable for use in design (rapid development, but much duplication of effort at universities and poor communication of research results)

Effects of wave climate, currents, beaches, shorelines of dredging inshore sand and offshore gravel (little progress)

Effects of contaminated discharges from outfalls and improved design of diffuser outlets (problems of saline intrusion and of fouling have been studied; inspection and maintenance now becoming important; an important and commercially active topic)

Nearshore hydrodynamics, including wave forces, wave grouping, resonance of structures, especially relevant to breakwater design (considerable discussion and improvement in application of hydrodynamics to breakwater design)

Foundations on coastal sediments, including armoured slopes (some progress, but an urgent need for research on design of foundations for flexible concrete block revetments, and on scour at toes of revetments and seawalls)

Sediment dynamics, especially in dredged channels, tidal inlets, estuaries (continuous progress but still a priority requirement; erosion of saltings and mud flats now an urgent issue)

Design and effectiveness of groyne systems for coast protection (major research has highlighted difficulties; advances made, but no categorical conclusions yet attained)

New methods for hydraulic discharge of fine materials for offshore reclamation (little progress, hampered by changing legislation and pollution standards)

Principles of design for beach nourishment and stability (no scientific principles for design yet exist; monitoring of actual projects should be co-ordinated and coupled with more fundamental research)

Uses of very fine or polluted dredged sediments (little advance; an increasingly important subject area)

Instrumentation for marine data collection, especially for remote monitoring under exposed conditions (progress in gaining reliable data on open coasts; further progress expected)

Monitoring and evaluation of coast protection schemes in practice (uncoordinated; needs to include assessment of maintenance requirements, and provide detailed information)

Low-cost shore protection methods for overseas uses (slow progress on account of reluctance to accept low-technology solutions; now also seen to be relevant to UK)

Improved understanding of statistics of joint probability of interrelated extreme events (in progress, but depends on acquisition of extensive data sets; also very important for offshore structures)

Physical processes of shorelines of cohesive sediments, including unstable cliffs (a newly recognised need that has received little research study)

Weathering and protection of sedimentary rock cliffs (a new topic that should include use of geotextiles and re-establishment of vegetation)

Use and performance of new and traditional materials in marine environments (a new topic, that should include comparative performance of different timbers, and evaluation of nylon, polypropylene and so on)

Offshore islands (tombolos) as a means of reversing coast erosion (a new topic; economics and practicability need research; a large market for application if viable)

8.3.2.	*Defence installations*	Criteria for jetty design, including loadings from berthing vessels and wind forces from moored ships (a perennial problem, especially as ship designs change; should include fendering and underwater protection)

Painting below water line (review of practice and practical trials)

Methods of ship-to-shore waste disposal to avoid discharges into harbours and estuaries (research carried out; not an active requirement)

Development of more effective oil traps

Design of structures to withstand high explosive attack

Effect of chemical and bacteriological warfare on water supplies and sewage treatment

Methods of reliable costing of major and complex projects (still a high priority; should include estimation of maintenance requirements and probable economic life)

8.3.3.	*Offshore structures (gas and oil)*	Pipe-laying techniques in up to 100 m water depths, particularly trenching and connections (some progress, but research still needed; design of riser systems and subsea chokes a current need; design for Arctic conditions needs special attention)

Mechanisms of fatigue failure in steel offshore structures (research in progress but a long way from a full understanding)

Use of 'explosive methods' to form foundation connections (not now required; other methods now used)

Removal of offshore structures (development of techniques and equipment required to meet international legislation; an opportunity for UK to take the lead)

Equipment and techniques for deep-sea site investigation (good progress, but foreseen expansion with deeper water has not happened; techniques not fully developed)

Design of tension piles (significant progress; work still required on stress reversal)

Behaviour of pile groups (full-scale field tests have provided good understanding, but still major gaps; present conservative design interpretation does not cause major additional costs)

General design of piles for deep-sea sites and soils (design factors still incompletely defined. Priority areas are: skin friction in clays; lateral behaviour in stiff clay; end bearing of piles in sand and carbonate soils behaviour)

Single point moorings in deep water (research still required on mooring dynamics and design)

Floating platforms (computer design systems still needed for up to 2000 m water depths, including effects of drift and wind; design effects of wind need much research)

Subsea production systems (methods of installation and maintenance; a great amount of research into subsea diverless template in progress)

Monitoring structural peformance (large offshore structures should be fully monitored and the results disseminated)

Pipeline trenching in shifting seabed conditions (new topic)

8.3.4.	*Offshore structures (other than oil)*	In the case of the first ten research topics, the requirements remain unchanged; many items are also applicable to gas and oil offshore structures.

Physical properties of construction materials, and development of new materials for long-term durability at offshore sites

Methods of lowering large masses/structures in deep water

Numerical prediction of dynamic response of flexible structures in open sea

Optimal design of pressurised vessels by analytical methods

Improvement of sea-bed sampling and foundation design for cyclic loading

Improved methods for repair of structures in service

Improved means of collection/interpretation of site data

Review of types of contract appropriate to offshore structures

Sealing and safety of sub-seabed shafts

Methods of processing/handling minerals from offshore platforms

Deepwater dredging for mineral nodules (research has been suspended)

8.3.5.	*Ports and harbours*	Wave recording: improved instrumentation and forecasting techniques (progress being made, particularly in computer-based predictions — needs to be susbtained; also relevant to offshore structures; should cross-fertilise with platform monitoring)

Ships and ship behaviour in channels and exposed berths (advances in model simulation need to be sustained)

Siltation, channel maintenance and disposal of dredged sediments (an area of active research with increasing importance in respect of deeper channel requirements and legislative restrictions on dredged sediment disposal)

Breakwater design and maintenance (actively researched, disseminated and discussed, but some major failures highlight serious weaknesses in knowledge that need to be rectified; an important subject area)

Design and instrumentation of quay walls and other earth-retaining structures

New methods of paving (new methods of heavy duty paving have emerged, with the active involvement of the British Ports Authority)

Design and operation of port storage facilities (silos and containers) (not a high priority)

Construction materials in marine conditions (corrosion of steel and suitability of aggregates; deserves more attention as maintenance costs mount)

Design for minimum maintenance and prediction of maintenance costs (design should now take into account shorter necessary life of port facilities; review impact of this on design criteria and objectives)

Design, operation and repair of Ro-Ro link spans (new topic)

8.3.6.	*Shipyards (building and repair)*	No major research needs are identified, but a state-of-the-art review on design and fixing of quay-side crane rails to support heavy wheel loads would be welcomed.

8.3.7.	*Thermal power stations*	Construction and performance of chimneys

Development of plume-free cooling towers

Optimum layout of cooling water systems to minimise recirculation and environmental effects; design/materials to reduce marine growth (considerable progress in computer modelling of thermal discharges needs to be continued, particularly in terms of environmental effects; problem of marine growth remains)

Foundations for large steam turbo-alternator sets

Boiler structures and box columns

Alternative fuels

8.3.8.	*Tidal energy structures and tidal barriers*	Hydrodynamics of jets discharged from turbines, including computer modelling (also relevant to non-energy barrages; still required)

Computer modelling of dispersion in 2 and 3 dimensions (considerable progress; still a priority)

Faster and cheaper 2-d and 3-d computer models of complex tidal waters (much progress, exploiting new hardware; also of use for offshore structures)

Performance of very large flap gates, including wave effects

Design criteria for wave loading over a very long structure

Propagation of deep-water waves into shallow coasts with complex topography (advances in modelling)

Influence of draft tube geometry on performance of turbines and sluices

Influence of waves on turbine performance and control

Methods of embankment closure against tidal action (also relevant to non-tidal works; still required)

Mixing/stratification of influent waters

8.3.9. Wave energy structures

The first seven research topics are also relevant to coastal and maritime civil engineering and, apart from the first item, to design of offshore structures. Their need and priority is not dependent upon a wave energy programme.

Wave attenuation in shallow waters

Directionality of wave data

Breaking wave forces

Data on offshore sea currents

Inhibition of marine growth on marine structures

Fatigue of concrete structures in a maritime environment

Corrosion and fatigue of steel structures in a maritime environment

Moorings and anchorage for wave energy structures (this topic is also very important for floating production systems offshore; much research and development is in progress)

Techniques for mathematical analysis of wave energy devices

Production engineering of repetitive units for wave energy devices

8.3.10. Electronics

The pace of development in electronics in the past few years has made the R&D requirements in the 1981 Task Force Report almost obsolete. Research in this subject area is generally well covered by commercial developers, although the boundaries of application and general reliability of electronic systems need to be given attention. In the maritime field there is scope for more refinement in automated and unmanned hydrographic surveying, and in automated dredging control (which is largely being commercially developed by Dutch dredger builders). In maritime applications, the greatest concern is that electronic devices should be robust, reliable and waterproof in a corrosive environment. However, this is identified as an area of weakness in which some practical research and development would be welcomed by the user industry.

8.3.11. Numerical methods

The 1981 Task Force Report has also been overtaken by developments in the area of numerical methods. A wide range of software packages is available for both structural design and simulation of tidal processes. For the offshore industry, further research is required into the application of probabilistic methods to structural design, and means for optimisation. In the modelling of tidal processes, there remains a strong need for models that comprehensively address current, wave and sediment processes in the inshore zone. The incorporation of biological and chemical environmental processes into hydrodynamic models is now becoming a high priority. There is an underlying and growing concern that complex numerical models are insufficiently validated against real data. As a high priority, baseline data need to be acquired for validation of computer-based models.

9.   TRANSPORT

9.1.   Introduction

Transport differs from some other sectors under consideration in several important respects. Firstly, it is an area almost exclusively of public sector responsibility; thus governments, both central and local, together with the relevant public sector organisations, are almost the sole recipients of research findings and, through their actions, are most likely to stimulate or stifle innovation. Secondly, the benefits of transport decisions are widely distributed throughout the community, are rarely recouped by the decision maker and are often intangible in nature; this, in turn, places considerable emphasis on the development of appraisal techniques. Thirdly, most applications of research are one-off, and it is difficult therefore to patent the results of research initiatives and hence pay for the initial research activity, thus strengthening the case for government support. Fourthly, most decisions on the use of transport systems are made by individuals, whose demands are difficult to control, and are expected to grow rapidly; it is estimated, for example, that use of UK roads will grow by up to 33 per cent by the year 2000, and that in the same period the number of cars in cities of the developed world will increase by 70 per cent. Finally, the operation of the transport system is a major element in the civil engineer's responsibilities; this not only imposes a major emphasis on research programmes, but it also introduces the involvement into those programmes of a number of other disciplines.

9.2.   Market prospects

Within the UK, transport infrastructure generally is expanding much less rapidly than demand. The total length of road is growing at about 0·5 per cent per annum while road use is rising at about 3 per cent per annum; airport passenger numbers are expected to double by the year 2000, primarily using existing facilities. This will place far greater emphasis on improving efficiency in the use of existing infrastructure, and maintaining its fitness for purpose. At the same time, it will be important to ensure that investment in new infrastructure is put to the best use. In general, emphasis must be on:

- improving efficiency, bearing in mind that the total resource costs of operating and using the transport system represent some 20 per cent of Gross National Product

- extending the life of existing infrastructure, in spite of the increasing load imposed by heavier and hence more damaging vehicles

- increasing the contribution of transport to economic regeneration and new development

- improving safety, against a background of around 1/3 million injuries a year

- reducing the impact on the environment

- improving energy efficiency in a sector which now accounts for almost 60 per cent of all oil consumption.

Within the individual subsectors, several developments have taken place since 1981 which affect future market prospects.

In the road subsector, the decision on the Channel Fixed Link will introduce new pressures; completion of the M25 has introduced new concern over our ability to manage high capacity roadways; new interest has been generated in private financing for, for example, the Dartford Tunnel; there is growing realisation of the need for comprehensive approaches to tackling urban problems, but abolition of the metropolitan counties and deregulation of bus services are making this more difficult to achieve; information technology developments have offered new opportunities for improved use of the highway; maintenance expenditure has failed to keep pace with need, with the result that defect levels are now 20 per cent higher on urban principal roads and 15 per cent higher on rural roads than they were in 1980.

In the rail subsector, the Channel Fixed Link decision, new electrification projects and renewed interest in cross-London and airport links provide opportunities for infrastructure improvement; growing enthusiasm for light rapid transit may lead to new types of infrastructure requirement; British Rail's change in management style introduces new opportunities for engineers to contribute to business development; the track maintenance backlog has fallen, but problems of bridge maintenance appear to be growing.

In the airports subsector, deregulation and the Airports White Paper jointly strengthen the case for further investment in the provincial airports and for greater emphasis on surface access.

The developing world is a particularly important market for transport. Transport represented around 30 per cent of civil engineering overseas earnings in 1985, and demand for transport is likely to grow much more rapidly than in the UK. The poor state of current infrastructure, the lack of local skills and shortage of finance all place emphasis on provision of low cost infrastructure, simple but efficient traffic management, and labour-intensive maintenance. Many of the solutions will therefore be different from those in the UK, and the emphasis must be on modifications to provide appropriate technology. Conversely, the developed world is likely to provide a market only for specialist infrastructure and high technology facilities; the USA, for example, is investing in automated light rapid transit, but is buying French expertise with which the UK currently cannot compete.

The second report of the ICE Infrastructure Planning Group indentifies many of these issues and, in addition, stresses the need for improved interchange between modes, and more consistent objectives for, and assessment of, individual modes.

A confidential report by the ICE's Engineering Committee, 'The Role of the Engineer in Repair and Maintenance, including these Matters as a Factor in Design', is another important source of information on research requirements in this area.

9.3.   Research priorities

In general, the nature of the transport sector, as outlined above, places greater emphasis on the estimation of demand for transport, the use of transport facilities, and the evaluation of the costs and benefits to society of transport decisions. These emphases are reflected in the research priorities identified in the following paragraphs. Highest priority requirements are given in italics but the relative priorities of other items will occassionally require re-assessment.

9.3.1.   Assembly of physical data

Research needs arise for the monitoring of the current state, use and adequacy of the transport system, prediction of future demand, and appraisal of alternative solutions. The major needs are as follows.

Improved data bases for infrastructure condition monitoring

The development of problem-orientated monitoring techniques

Application of information technology to data collection and monitoring

Non-destructive testing techniques for airport runways, drawing on current work in highway pavement testing

Improved methods of traffic forecasting to incorporate the effects of congestion and new infrastructure

Assessment of the effects of transport on economic growth

Improved understanding of the interaction between city form, demand for travel and choice of appropriate mode, *particularly in developing countries*

The effects of telecommunications on travel

The demand implications of the Channel Fixed Link

The future implications for transport of fuel availability

Improved techniques for environmental impact assessment

The incorporation of uncertainty into appraisal techniques

The development of common methodologies for inter-modal comparison of track costs and investment benefits

9.3.2.   Materials

The main issues concern pavement materials for airports and roads, where the issues are fairly similar, and track requirements for railways. The major needs are as follows.

The performance of pavement materials in use

The use of waste materials and recycling

The use of low cost indigenous materials, particularly in developing countries

Improved mixes for both bituminous and cement-bound materials

The durability of skid resistant materials

The use of concrete blocks for runways

Improved specifications for rail steel

The loading performance of different ballasts

In the longer term it will be necessary to add:

The appropriateness of alternative transport fuels

9.3.3.   Analysis and design

The issues under this heading include transport system design, analysis of vehicle-infrastructure interaction, and pavement/track design. The main needs are as follows.

The development of integrated approaches to urban transport planning, encompassing road construction, traffic management and land use

The review of the primary route network

Redesign to accommodate higher flows, maintenance and emergencies

Improved analysis of vehicle/track interaction and the effects of active suspension

Analysis of the aerodynamics of trains in tunnels

Reduction of noise and vibration from railways

Whole-life cost design techniques for roads

Improved procedures for runway design

Treatment or avoidance of joints in runways

Simulation techniques for track layout

The development of more cost-effective electrification and provision of jointless track circuits

New track forms for light rail and magnetically levitated vehicles

Low energy tunnel ventilation systems

Design of less visually intrusive light rail structures.

9.3.4.	*Construction*	Few issues directly related to construction have been raised. The main needs are as follows.

Improved compaction techniques for runways

The further development of soft ground tunnelling techniques (to compete with the Japanese)

Techniques for the more rapid construction of overhead light rail structures

Reassessment of the benefits of staged construction for roads

The development of labour intensive methods for use in the developing world.

9.3.5.	*Use*	A long list of requirements has been identified, particularly for improved use of the transport system which, as noted above, is a key element of the responsibilities of civil engineers in the transport sector. The main needs are as follows.

Further research into road safety, particularly for vulnerable users

Techniques for the management of traffic on high capacity roads

The development of route guidance and in-vehicle information systems

The development of automated highways

Improved efficiency in freight management

Control of heavy vehicles to reduce pavement damage

The development of passenger information systems

The use of information technology techniques for public transport management

Assessment of the operational costs and benefits of automated light rapid transit

Treatment of fuel spillage on runways

The effects of de-icing compounds on runways

Maintenance of skid resistance on runways

In the maintenance area, the needs are as follows.

Treatment of road salt damage to structures

The development of maintenance management systems

Programming methods for maintenance while retaining infrastructure use

Treatment of concrete joints in roadways and, more imporatntly, *in runways*

The development of improved track maintenance methods.

10.   WATER ENGINEERING

10.1.   Introduction

In this Chapter, a summary is given of market prospects, together with lists of research needs, in five important areas of civil engineering. These five areas are:

- dams and reservoirs (excluding hydropower)
- water supply (treatment and distribution)
- sewerage and sewage treatment
- irrigation and land drainage
- waterways.

In addition, a section considers waste disposal — including reclaimed land — and its potential effect on the water cycle.

Altogether, work in these areas accounts for over 25 per cent of all overseas earnings by British civil engineering consultants and contractors and about 20 per cent of all civil engineering work in the UK. It is estimated that in the UK the total annual expenditure on research and development in these areas is around £7 million — that is, about 0.7 per cent of turnover.

The Task Force Report pointed to the designation by the United Nations of the World Water Decade as:

'Recognition that water was man's most basic need and resource, and that most of the world's population lack a clean water supply and the related facility of hygienic sewage and waste disposal.'

10.2.   Dams and reservoirs (excluding hydropower)

The demand for water is generally falling in the UK, although in Northern Ireland, for example, the Government is now considering schemes to develop further yields. It is clear that the number of new dams and major reservoirs likely to be built in the UK is limited, although more tailings (the fine residual material resulting from mining and mineral processing) dams might be constructed.

Research into tailings dams has become a high priority. The recent failure of a tailings dam in Italy highlighted the potential dangers with such dams and the need for proper planning, design, construction and subsequent inspection.

In Great Britain, the implementation of the Reservoirs Act 1975 has caused a great deal of attention to be paid to the safety of existing dams and embankments, as well as to that of new structures. Although the Act does not apply to Northern Ireland, its principles have been adopted by the Department of the Environment (Northern Ireland) Water Service. As with the 1930 Act, the new Act requires an inspection of the structure generally every ten years but adds the requirement that the owner appoint a Panel Engineer to provide continual supervision between the statutory inspections.

In the UK there is increasing pressure from environmental groups against construction. Overseas, particularly in developing countries, this is generally not the case as the needs of expanding populations tend to be paramount. Work is being done within the International Commission on Large Dams (ICOLD) to try to quantify environmental impact by a uniform type of environmental impact statement on the economic and financial aspects of project planning.

Overseas the market for British consulting engineers remains strong; projects are chiefly multi-purpose for river regulation, flood control and hydropower. The competition for work overseas, however, is now even stronger.

Although the planning and implementation of major dam or reservoir projects take place inevitably over a long period, study of environmental issues which may impede construction should take place in the earliest stages.

Advances in flood estimation resulting from better understanding of hydrological data affect the design of diversion structures and flood spillways. Similarly, an understanding of seismic risks in many parts of the world demands more stringent design of structures to resist seismic effects. These, and other considerations such as environmental impact of dams and reservoirs and the importance of the safety of such structures, place heavy responsibilities on the designers.

Numerical modelling is already used in design, and it reduces reliance on physical models. A programme to improve the correlation between mathematical models and physical models would be an extremely valuable aid to the design of high-head hydraulic structures. Some work has started in this area which should provide a relatively cheap tool for the redesign of spillways, not infrequently required by inspecting engineers.

There is a need for further development of analytical techniques as design tools for the prediction of the behaviour of dams and their components when subject to earthquakes. A considerable amount of relevant work has already been done in the UK, but there appears to be a need to correlate the results of the various groups involved.

Finite element analysis techniques for the evaluation of stresses in fill dams are now well known, but some advances have been made in the analysis following the Carsington Dam failure. This, in turn, has identified further analytical needs, particularly their application to various types of fill dam.

Some work has been carried out on flow through and overtopping of rockfill dams but further work in this area is justified. Rockfill dams are sometimes used as cofferdams as the diversion phase of major dams. Designed for a limited life and to withstand floods with much greater exceedance frequency than the main dam, these cofferdams can provide an opportunity to study failure under full-scale conditions.

At the fifteenth ICOLD Congress, the instrumentation of dams was discussed, and it is clear that there is room for further development in the design of instruments. At present, many instruments are abandoned soon after the construction period and are not capable of restoration.

The problem of alkali-silica reaction in concrete has become very apparent on dams. Work on this problem is proceeding in various organisations, but establishing some rapid test for the onset of the phenomenon would be invaluable, as would methods of controlling the situation when it occurs.

With regard to the newer materials, there is still scope for research into problems encountered with dispersive soils, core deterioration and soil-cement. Also, a number of the newer materials — such as rolled concrete — have been used in dams and embankments in recent years. It would be valuable if an internationally accepted system could be developed for the long-term monitoring of such structures.

Much of the research suggested in the original Task Force Report now forms part of the Department of the Environment (DoE) (Water Directorate) Research on Reservoir Safety. The programme is relatively new but includes work on:

- reservoir safety probabilistic risk assessment
- flood hazards over reservoired areas
- reinforcement of steep grassed waterways
- numerical modelling of high-velocity flow (including calibration on various sites)
- modes of dam failure
- flooding and flood damage following dam failure
- relationships between storm precipitation and flooding
- wave prediction in reservoirs
- protection of embankment dam faces against wave attack
- internal pressure and uplift on massive concrete dams
- safety of embankment dams
- acute variations in time and space of rainfall in upland areas.

A list of additional research requirements is shown in Section 10.9.1.

10.3. Water supply (treatment and distribution)

In the UK, it is unlikely that there will be many demands for substantial new sources of water supply within the next twenty years. Increasing attention is being paid to the more efficient use of water, both domestically and industrially (to reduce water and effluent charges). Nevertheless, long-term planning to meet needs beyond the end of the century is even more important now than when the Task Force Report was written, bearing in mind the long lead time needed to implement schemes.

In the UK, the main need is for major maintenance, repair, updating or complete reconstruction of existing treatment plants and major sections of the distribution systems. This is paralleled by programmes for improving the maintenance and operating techniques in developing countries by providing assistance and training from the UK and other developed areas.

The market potential for overseas work is considerable and there will inevitably be requirements for substantial additional water supplies, particularly in the Middle and Far East, Africa and South America. Overseas, particularly in the developing countries, new sources need to be realised, although it is likely that these will be smaller local schemes rather than grandiose schemes.

The need to reduce energy use and improve quality suggests more use of upland sources. Schemes with heavy pumping components are not likely to be viable (e.g. large pumped storage or estuarial barrage schemes). The main improvements in operation are likely to arise from the combined use of ground and surface water and the collection and processing of data to maximise the use of the most economical source to be utilised.

The use of alternative fuels is of growing significance in many areas of the developing world. Apart from alcohol or hydrogen, the possible use of diesel derived from palm oil is of current interest.

Greater operational control of the system, which could include the treatment works, may lead to considerable reduction in costs and this will involve more widespread use of instrumentation for monitoring and control. Some progress has been made into the effective use of data-links and microprocessors. Further development should lead to considerable savings in pumping costs.

Groundwater sources should be used to the limit of exploitation.

This will need more application of artificial recharge, aquifer control and river augmentation schemes.

Considerable work has been carried out in cleaning up rivers and improving the operation of sewage treatment works, although much still remains to be done. The whole river basin needs to be considered as an entity and the Water Research Centre (WRc) are now undertaking a River Basin Management Programme.

The main problems with water treatment will continue to be the removal of solids and sterilisation. Overseas, where many of the sources are rivers with heavy silt load at certain times of the year, the main problem will be the removal of these silts, settlement and filtration.

There has been a fundamental re-appraisal of water resource development in the UK in recent years, including much greater emphasis on the use of groundwater. Large-scale surface reservoirs are no longer popular and other options have to be explored before such schemes are permitted. Demand forecasting needs to be more accurate and work is required to correlate water usage with environmental factors.

There has been a significant increase in the use of bottled water that may indicate a quite different approach to water quality standards for potable water and perhaps a need to re-think the standards necessary for water treatment.

Intensive efforts are being made by the water industry on leakage control. A significant achievement has been the completion of a system for controlling water leakage by combined metering at Plymouth. Metering of supplies is being considered on a large scale and this could prove important, bearing in mind the possible privatisation of the Water Authorities.

Concern is continuing over river intakes, as they are liable to pollution resulting from accidental spillage, illegal discharges and agricultural operations, and there is a need for reliable and easily-maintained monitors (e.g. for ammonia, phenols, pH) and methods of intake protection. Also, there will be greater need for raw water bankside storage, both as a stage of treatment and as a defence against accidental pollution. Although most treatment processes are well established, there is a need to update existing plants. There is also a need to consider a method of treatment for lowland river sources for problems not encountered in upland supply, e.g. the presence of toxic metals, pesticides, nitrates, etc.

There has probably never been a period of greater world-wide concern for the environment than at present. In the face of increasing environmental legislation, it is important to maintain a supportable scientific approach to its derivation and implementation. EEC Regulations are now being drafted which will require the removal of nitrates and other substances from potable water supplies. The sterilisation of viruses is a cause for concern and requires further investigation. The cost of controlling these substances to comply with the EEC drinking water directives could involve great practical difficulties and expenditure. Much of the work at the WRc is directed towards satisfying EEC and other standards.

A list of research needs is shown in Section 10.9.2.

10.4.   Sewerage and sewage treatment

For the most part, the UK has satisfied a large part of its need for water supply and waste removal, treatment and disposal. Relatively few industrialised nations have reached a similar position and this includes the USA, France and Belgium. Earlier forecasts of increasing water demand have been revised to indicate slower growth and there is now more emphasis on conservation and avoidance of waste. The implications of the Control of Pollution Act (in Northern Ireland, the Water Act (NI) 1972) and EEC Regulations are relevant.

The situation overseas is different and highly variable. The impact of the UN Water Decade has certainly resulted in some increase in investment in waste disposal in the less developed countries. In developing countries, as provision is made for more adequate water supplies, there will be a corresponding need to provide means for the collection and disposal of domestic wastes, which will be satisfied only as fast as social and economic policies permit.

There have been a number of significant developments since the Task Force Report was published, which are — not necessarily in order of importance — as follows.

- Of major concern is the announcement by the Government of its intention to privatise the Regional Water Authorities. The implications of this are difficult to assess without some indication of what form privatisation might take, but one result could be the metering of domestic supplies leading to an overall lowering of consumption and consequent stronger sewage.

- Recommendations to improve coastal water quality in the vicinity of bathing beaches have been made in reports from the Royal Commission on Environmental Protection.

- Each year, the water industry produces around 35 million wet tonnes of sewage sludge. Of particular concern, therefore, is the increasing pressure from the EEC in respect of sludge disposal and also on the need to improve coastal water quality adjacent to bathing beaches. EEC legislation is now being drafted which will require the removal of nitrates and other substances from some sewage.

- The Report of the National Steering Group on Instrumentation, Control and Automation (ICA) indicates that the potential for exploiting ICA within the water industry is enormous. The general trend towards greater automation and remote control will expand considerably over the next five years.

- A useful market is being developed overseas by joint consultants/WRc activity in Advanced Water Technology (AWT) which comprises the management and renovation of water distribution and sewage collection systems.

- Within the industry, work on standards, quality assurance, evaluation/testing and the need for improved instrumentation has highlighted the potential benefits from a 'coherent purchasing policy'. These benefits include more reliable products, reduced costs and products which meet specific needs.

On account of reduced flow forecasts, the present market trend in the UK is towards rehabilitation and maintenance rather than towards new work, in particular to maintain and upgrade the ageing sewerage system. The WRc has provided the methodology and guidance on materials and techniques for rehabilitation. About half the capital expenditure in the UK water industry is spent on the rehabilitation of sewers and water mains.

There is greater awareness of the social costs associated with trenching works, and trenchless pipe-laying methods are being actively promoted as part of the development of new relining and replacement techniques.

Many treatment works constructed in the first half of this century will need to be updated, renovated or repaired. At many small works, operational problems need to be resolved, particularly as manning levels are reduced or visits made less frequently.

The advent of the Control of Pollution Act has brought about a thorough review of effluent standards by the Regional Water Authorities, and a substantial amount has been spent, and will continue to be spent, on raising the standard of effluents from sewage treatment works. Regional and national strategies for the utilisation or disposal of sludge will also be of continual importance.

The strict financial controls imposed by Government in recent years have led to the search for low operating cost plants. Increased automation has brought reductions in operating costs together with extensive demanning, and the trend to more extensive use of ICA is positive. The Government now seems to be embarking on a new energy management programme which will influence designers when they are considering new plants, particularly package plants which tend to be heavy energy users. However, package plants tend to be favoured by small communities, and developments in their use will continue.

A list of research needs is shown in Section 10.9.3.

10.5. Irrigation and land drainage

Any changes in irrigation and drainage development will probably arise mainly from changes in agricultural and horticultural methods at the field level. The main development will be overseas. Figures show that the value of work in hand overseas for consulting engineers has increased by around four times in the period from 1982 to 1985. Development in the UK, however, will generally be small scale and installed on the initiatives of individual farmers; this will also be true of Northern Europe and the USA.

The main factors that could create a greater demand for work are:

– increasing shortage of suitable water for agriculture

– high cost and availability of energy sources

– realisation that small-scale schemes with simple operation and maintenance requirements are more viable in some developing countries than large-scale projects

– increasing returns which are available to farmers who can produce high-quality crops out of the main production season; this requires careful control of the soil/water/nutrient environment; in addition, lack of best-quality land will mean that less easily-developed land will have to be utilised which may necessitate changing the topography using earth-moving equipment.

Health problems arising from changes in environmental conditions caused by large-scale developments, particularly overseas, have been recognised. Solutions require to be developed in terms of alternative strategies and to be evaluated in both economic and social terms.

Since the Task Force Report was produced in 1981, there has been no significant change in engineering solutions, techniques or materials used. The major change has been in the effect of the markets on the implementation of new techniques. This situation has been brought about by the increase in food production and surplus in most developed countries to such an extent that subsidies are required for their export. A similar pattern has occurred with energy and the effect of a rise in cost and shortage of energy resources seems less important now than it did in 1981.

In both developed and developing countries, the installation of irrigation and drainage facilities is sensitive to foodstuff prices and this will in turn affect the volume and direction of R&D. Obviously R&D

should take the longer-term view and not follow too closely the vagaries of the market-place.

In Northern Europe, much irrigation is in high-value crops rather than grains, and these crops may be less susceptible to the surplus problem.

There is still a world-wide market for engineering services and equipment for irrigation schemes. This is particularly true for developing countries where there is a lack of management skills to fulfil the potential of projects in the agricultural sector; this inhibits the rapid increase in crop production. Suppliers of hardware, such as pumps, will need to meet the requirements of lower energy use and ease of maintenance/repair. The use of solar power, particularly for the hotter countries, would seem to offer advantages.

Because of the easing of energy costs, the pressure to move from sprinkler to surface irrigation systems is less. However, many developing countries are short of foreign exchange necessary to import fuel, and therefore the cheaper forms of irrigation, such as surface irrigation, are more likely to be favoured. This has also meant that the introduction of large-scale irrigation facilities has slowed down. Many developing countries can obtain international loans for capital works at preferential rates of interest.

In the Middle East and Europe, centre pivot and linear move irrigators have now established themselves, and this has happened more quickly than was envisaged in 1981.

There has been rapid development of geotextiles and geomembranes, and the increased and wider use of these materials will continue. In agricultural drainage, the use of plastic drainage pipe has become more prevalent, taking over from concrete and clay tiles.

The use of precasting of small irrigation and drainage structures will increase and this may be coupled with the use of the newer materials such as GRP and GRC. The increasing use of newer materials makes even more important the need for long-term trials.

There has been a further recognisable shift in the emphasis from new projects to rehabilitation and from large-scale to small-scale projects.

The impetus to introduce low-head sprinkler systems will continue. The use of borehole supplies for irrigation, both in developed and developing countries should be pursued as this can offer economies.

A list of research needs is shown in Section 10.9.4.

10.6.   Waterways

Within the UK, waterways consist of the following:

- natural rivers and streams
- artificially-developed rivers
- artificial channels.

In addition to navigation, waterway systems provide the national infrastructure for: conservation and recreation; effluent disposal; fisheries; hydro-electric energy; land drainage and flood control; water resources and irrigation. Overseas, waterways also provide these functions, although the emphasis on different aspects will vary. The means of ownership, control and administration will also vary.

Experience suggests that although overseas work would not call for R&D studies differing in character from those foreseeable in connection with UK requirements, the scale of work overseas and the type of structure can vary enormously.

The structure of waterways research in the UK should present fewer problems than some other areas of civil engineering as the number of bodies with responsibility for waterways is small. Most of the waterways in the UK are the responsibility of the British Waterways Board (BWB) or the ten Regional Water Authorities (RWAs). In Scotland, the authorities responsible for rivers are now the twelve regional or island councils. In Northern Ireland, the Department of Agriculture (Drainage Division) is responsible for waterways.

The RWAs have a considerable commitment to research, mainly through the WRc. The work of the WRc does not, however, cover the function of the rivers as navigable waterways. The BWB budget for construction and maintenance has increased considerably over the past five years with the injection of substantial new Government grants. However, it is significant that although the 10-year corporate plan drawn up by the BWB for 1985-95 does contain provision for research, there is no money available under the present 3-year financial rolling programme.

A relevant research programme is that of the Ministry of Agriculture, Fisheries and Food (MAFF) on river and coastal engineering, with research directed mainly towards land drainage and flood protection, but including bank protection and erosion control. Other Government departments with responsibility for waterways include the Department of the Environment and the Department of Transport.

Although the size of the market for civil engineering in waterways is much smaller than in the earlier areas considered in this Chapter, there is worthwhile potential for growth.

UK waterways cannot compare in importance with those of north-west Europe. The German, Dutch, French and Belgians especially have much larger programmes of modern construction, improvement and maintenance of navigable waterways than the UK.

Although there is no general resurgence of commercial waterway traffic in the UK, there has been some development of the waterways in the North East, and the waterways in the East Midlands and Severn Basin appear to be attracting further commercial interests, both for existing industries and for new developments at locations alongside waterways.

Increased use of the waterways for industry could result from current development, mainly overseas, of transportation, handling and packaging systems. There is also a development of shallow-draft vessels which can use the European waterway system and now also the North Sea to reach UK ports. These could be inland ports on waterways. The implication of climatic change forecasts are that there will be higher sea levels and some port facilities may be unusable in the future.

The use of pipelines as an alternative means of transport is developing and this can affect the demand for waterways.

Recreational use of waterways continues to grow, placing an increasing requirement on water for cruising and locking. Additional waterway areas might be provided by bringing disused sections back into operation, such as has been done at the Kennet and Avon Canal, and the Montgomery Canal. Increased recreational use has exacerbated the problems of leakage and bank erosion.

A large number of bodies, including county and district councils, have entered into agreements with owners of waterways for the purpose of extending and giving financial support to amenity uses. Refurbishment of the canal system is recognised as a useful and appropriate application of youth training and opportunity schemes. Such schemes are being greatly expanded over the next two years.

The drought in 1976 demonstrated the need for water resource development and sufficient storage to meet anticipated requirements in dry years. Development may support navigation and water power as well as water for household, industrial and agricultural use, and may be combined with flow augmentation or flood control.

With rising energy costs, utilisation of the waterways to create energy — for example, in providing for tidal energy and use of small hydro-electric plant — is creating an expanding market overseas. There is considerable scope in the UK, particularly for tidal energy, although this could have significant effects on navigation and ecology.

Development of fish farming could have amenity as well as commercial benefit. Fisheries are highly dependent on water quality and acceptable flows. There is concern about the environmental impact of fish farming, and this has prompted a revision to codes of practice concerning good husbandry and the use of chemicals.

Aided by the decline in heavy industry, investment in sewage disposal has nearly eliminated class 4 pollution of inland rivers. If more stringent requirements were to be imposed, massive investment would be needed, particularly in storm sewerage systems. The main threat is from pollution caused by accidental spillages from industry and agricultural land, illicit trade effluent and storm overflows.

The need for flood control measures will increase with the spreading of urban areas and will stimulate the need for assessment of risk levels. The work of the Institute of Hydrology and Hydraulics Research Ltd in this area is particularly important.

Land drainage and flood control is the most capital-intensive activity in river systems. There is a need for greater sympathy for the environment in the design and implementation of land drainage schemes and this is being achieved with effective collaboration between water authorities and the statutory and voluntary bodies concerned. There is a growing awareness of the need to retain wetlands and to enhance wildlife and amenities when undertaking engineering works. Greater use of biological and polymer materials will aid more sympathetic design.

A list of research needs is shown in Section 10.9.5.

10.7.   Waste disposal

Of the 100 million tonnes or so of controlled wastes arising annually in the UK, over 90 per cent go directly to landfill. The remaining waste is treated in some way with the residue almost always going to landfill. None of this is necessarily a disadvantage as much of the landfill is, or can be, incorporated in schemes for land reclamation. Most farm waste and substantial quantities of sewage sludge are returned to the land as part of normal farming practice.

It seems likely that the quantity of domestic refuse will increase, and one suggested figure puts the quantity at 30 kg (10 kg at present) per week from the average household by the end of the century. However, the availability of land for waste disposal in the UK and in developed overseas countries is likely to diminish in the next decade, as sites become expensive to secure and to operate to required environmental standards.

The Control of Pollution Act 1974 had a considerable impact on the manner in which waste was disposed of, with the result that standards have improved. Part of the Act placed new duties on Waste Disposal Authorities (WDAs) regarding waste treatment, reclamation and disposal. It also provided for a licensing disposal system; one of the main purposes of the licensing system is the control of water pollution. Licenses are issued with various conditions and may include measures to deal with water pollution, leachate, monitoring and keeping records.

Under the Act, and before issuing a licence, the WDA has a statutory duty to consult with the water authority about the disposal of controlled waste at existing or new sites. At present, over 5000 licences are in operation.

However, the second report (1986) of the Hazardous Waste Inspectorate (HWI) lists examples of flagrant flouting of both the spirit and letter of the Act. The HWI report also indicates that there is an increasing quantity of hazardous wastes being imported to the UK from Europe for treatment and incineration. Other statistics show that landfill in 1985 accounted for 78·7 per cent of hazardous waste disposal. The disposal of hazardous wastes is a problem of growing concern to both the authorities and the public. Many wastes will need treatment to a greater degree than at present in specialised treatment plants and some can only be safely landfilled on sites taking large quantities of domestic and other refuse. The disposal of materials (some of which are classified as hazardous) from dust control systems can cause problems if discharged as a slurry as this could lead to contamination of groundwaters.

One of the most intractable problems associated with mining and mineral processing arises from the disposal of very fine residual material — tailings. This fine material is often disposed of by placing in a tailings dam, sometimes creating reservoirs, and this can cause problems of water pollution. Control of leachate and surface drainage from such sites is therefore particularly important. Although some research has been carried out, more is required, particularly field trials.

The production of methane in landfill sites and the potential dangers that it poses are well understood, and increasingly in the UK the gas is being tapped as an energy source. However, Government initiatives are required to promote this type of energy production. The recycling of materials is growing in importance and the processing of old deposits of municipal wastes may become viable for the recycling of metals.

For developing countries, landfill disposal is likely to continue as the most popular method of waste disposal. For the UK and developed countries overseas, important problems associated with waste disposal revolve around environmental factors and the sustained objections of a section of the public to the acceptance of landfilling as a method of disposal.

Accordingly, research work must concentrate on measures to improve the image of landfilling and to render the places of disposal safe insofar as water supplies are concerned. The same important requirement applies to nuclear waste disposal and both should be undertaken in parallel. More work is required on the behaviour of wastes within landfilled sites and the detailed mechanics of leachate production and attenuation within surrounding materials.

10.8. Land reclamation

In the UK, much urban derelict land awaits reclamation, and the need to use such land for residential, industrial development and for recreational purposes has reached a high priority. In certain cases, the value of fresh water for recreation will exceed the value of reclaimed land for other purposes.

Land available for reclamation includes land contaminated with toxic chemicals, some very seriously. Use of such land will require much greater attention to the quality of work, especially in reducing the effects of subsidence, interruption of drainage, and the avoidance, containment or neutralising of pollutants. Chapter 5 of this Report refers to the geotechnical problems involved. The costs of reclaiming such land is likely to be high.

Investigation of suitable designs for decommissioning on change of use of silt-filled reservoirs is of high priority. The recovered material can also be extremely valuable as topsoil for land reclamation elsewhere.

In developing countries, the need for reclaimed land, other than for food production, is likely to be small. Such reclamation could be linked to schemes for flood control, drainage, irrigation and polders. One area requiring high priority research concerns marginally arid land which has become degraded by climatic variables and greater pressure on the land resource itself.

Overseas, a top priority continues to be inter-country water resources and basin management studies applied to international river basins. A number of studies are now planned or in hand. It is particularly important to consider the effects on endemic water-related diseases such as malaria and schistosomiasis.

In both the UK and overseas, the trend will be towards increasing complexity of the investigation and will involve a greater understanding of the influence of ecological and social factors and of the various methods of controlling the effects of pollutants.

10.9. Research needs

The highest priority items identified in this review are given in italics, but the relative priorities of other items will occasionally require re-assessment.

10.9.1. Dams and reservoirs

Rip-rap design for wind and wave attack

Farm and small amenity reservoirs

Modification/calibration of 'DAMBRK'

Assessment of flood damage using 'DAMBRK'

Design, operation and maintenance of flood storage ponds

(The above items are included in the DoE (Water Directorate) Research on Reservoir Safety programme.)

Study of environmental issues (UK and overseas) likely to impede construction

Improve correlation between numerical and physical models

Correlate existing UK work on dam behaviour when subjected to earthquakes

Finite element analysis for various types of fill dam (post Carsington)

Flow-through and overtopping of rock-fill dams: field trials

Alkali-silica reaction in concrete dams: test for/control methods

Long-term monitoring of structures (UK and overseas)

Further development of instrumentation (including electronics)

Testing of materials (e.g. dispersive soils/core materials/soil-cement)

Sedimentation in reservoirs and density currents including selective withdrawal (overseas)

Aeration, cavitation and energy dissipation on dam spillways

10.9.2. Water supply (treatment and distribution)

10.9.2.1. Physical data

Processes of evaporation, infiltration and surface water run-off evaluation of aquifer parameters such as transmissivity and storage coefficients

Define more closely rainfall/run-off correlation particularly overseas

Evaluate the biological processes that take place during raw water storage and possible use of aeration as pre-treatment

Rationalisation of sources and economy in pumping costs

Uses of remote sensing and radar to improve levels of service and flood predictions

Continue research into biological processes in storage, treatment and distribution systems leading to a better understanding of the control of virus and bacteria

Monitor and observe fish movements

Assess the effects of obstructions on the overall regime of a river

Toxicity and other adverse effects of new materials on the water

Effect of chlorine on viruses

Alternative disinfecting agents and activated carbon treatment (in conjunction with medical research)

Strategic studies related to the protection of health from potentially hazardous substances

Effects of radioactive rain on drinking water supplies

10.9.2.2.   Materials

Control of coagulant and other chemical dosing rates combined with the recovery of alum

Developments of pipelines and fittings

Use of new and lighter material for pump manufacturers

Use of new materials, prefabrication and reduction in weight

Corrosion resistance of pipelines both internal and external (avoiding use of oil-based compounds as protection if possible)

Selection of pipeline materials

10.9.2.3.   Analysis and design

Removal of nitrates from drinking water

Development of ways of dealing with organic compounds in water, trihalomethane formation during chlorination, lead contamination in domestic plumbing, pollution by accidental spillage, sterilisation of viruses

Design of horizontal settlement tanks: hydraulic flow characteristics and more effective and reliable methods of desludging

Design and application of slow sand filtration for use in UK and overseas

Advanced chemical treatment for specialised industrial requirements

Pump design for simpler assembly and maintenance

Identification of chemical or other methods for removal of contaminants in an aquifer (e.g. oil or acid spillages)

Recovery of useful materials from industrial effluent

Saving water in industrial processes

Design of weirs: simplified low-cost installations in areas where there is no existing gauging

Calibration of existing weirs and installation of new structures

Conjunctive use of reservoirs, river and underground sources

Methods of treating moorland waters with algal growths

Dewatering sludge and recovery of alum

Uprating of existing treatment works

Methods of protection of intakes against accidental spillage, illegal discharges and agricultural operations

Innovation on intake design

Risk analysis to define design parameters (leading to smaller stage sizes and more flexible designs)

Equipment to monitor and establish levels of service

10.9.2.4. Construction

Development of more reliable, accurate and easily maintainable instruments for monitoring the quality of source water or of river and lake intakes, and for data analysis and control systems including microprocessors to use the information in operation, incorporating expert systems in appropriate areas

Development of more reliable and effective flow meters including better methods for maintenance and calibration (this would be particularly relevant if there were further political pressure to install water meters)

Assess the viability and effectiveness of new tunnelling methods

Trenchless methods for pipe laying

Modular construction methods to increase plant capacity in small stages

10.9.2.5. Use

Rehabilitation of mains

Durability of both existing and new mains under operating conditions including an assessment of current testing methods

Repair and renewal of water tunnels

Waste detection

Increased automatic control of distribution systems, with linking of digital mapping and data bases to facilitate this and to optimise day-to-day management and operation

Extension of the use of ICA

Operation and management of water mains

10.9.2.6. Other

Market research into the requirements and development of appropriate pumps for the required purpose in developing countries

Development of alternative fuels

River basin management

Studies of engineering and economic lessons and other experience to be learnt from completed projects

10.9.3. Sewerage and sewage disposal

10.9.3.1. Physical data

Risk assessment of urban surface water drainage

Polluting effects of surface water drainage and overflows from combined sewers

Continual assessment of water quality objectives

Cost-effectiveness of systems for use overseas

Quantify health and safety benefits of first-time sewerage overseas

Develop logical analyses for system design for UK and overseas to enable optimisation in respect of sewage and treatment works, effluent disposal, water management and sludge disposal and utilisation.

10.9.3.2. Materials

Resistance to corrosion of materials subject to septic sewage

Protection of iron and steel against corrosion

Long-term service properties of sewer pipe materials

Materials for use in specific localities

Selection of pipeline materials

10.9.3.3. Analysis/Design

Forecasting rainfall duration and estimating run-off percentages in relation to type and condition of surface and rainfall characteristic for surface water drainage

Design of on-line and off-line storage of surface water

Treatment of surface water drainage and storm sewage before discharge to water courses

Low-cost alternatives to conventional sewerage systems

Design of inlet works

Low-cost and simple treatment methods

Low-energy treatment methods

Development of low-energy, compact and odourless systems for sewage treatment

Removal of nutrients

Monitoring the performance of tunnels

Improved understanding of the chemistry and microbiology of sewage treatment, odour suppression and removal of pathogenic micro-organisms

Design and construction using indigenous materials and labour

Beneficial re-use of liquid and solid residues

Treatment of specific industrial wastes

Evaluate the potential expert systems

Piling behaviour, ground consolidation and groundwater problems when siting works in low-lying ground

Design of water-retaining structures particularly for durability (important overseas on account of severe weather conditions and poor aggregates)

Sewage Treatment Optimisation Model (STOM): enhancement

Design of sewage-retaining structures to a less stringent code than BS 5337 (water-retaining structures)

Design of long sludge pumping mains at high concentrations of suspended solids

Innovation and evaluation of new treatment processes (at full scale)

High rate sludge digestion

Dewatering of sewage sludge and handling thicker sludge

Sewage disposal to sea (high rate screening/disinfection plant)

Sediment movement in sewers and impact on receiving streams

Water quality modelling in sewers

Water quality modelling in rivers

10.9.3.4. Construction

Relationship between client, designer, equipment supplier and contractor in turnkey type contracts

Co-ordination of civil design, plant supply and operation requirements — forms of contract especially for work overseas

Advantages/disadvantages of sub-contracts for treatment works equipment

Trenchless methods for pipe laying

Economic and effective methods of excavation and back-fill for sewer construction

Problems in the use of large diameter flexible pipes, particularly overseas

Comparisons between pipes and tunnels, including settlement and response (overseas) to seismic shock

Improvement in tunnel linings and better methods of waterproofing

10.9.3.5. Use

Maintenance and repair of sewers

Renovation of ageing sewage treatment works

Methods of updating treatment processes

Control of odour from sewage and treatment works and disposal of sludge

Noise from sewage treatment plant installations

Environmental factors related to the disposal of liquid wastes and sludge to sea

Education and training in the maintenance and operation of sewerage systems

Financial development in under-developed countries

Long-term behaviour and durability of both new and traditional construction materials and components

Extension of the use of ICA

Sludge treatment (including flocculation, suppression of odour and removal of pathogenic micro-organisms) and disposal

Operation and management of sewerage systems

10.9.3.6. Other

Standards

Quality assurance

Evaluation/testing

10.9.4. Irrigation and land drainage

Note must be made of the Report on Irrigation, produced in February 1986 by the Fellowship of Engineering, which arose out of the Task Force Report. This report drew on the views of the full spectrum of UK engineers involved in irrigation and defined as a desirable national research programme on irrigation, and has given rise to an initiative to form an irrigation research club.

10.9.4.1.   Hydrology and soils

Collection of hydrological data relevant to irrigation

Modelling of rainfall/infiltration/run off and saturated/unsaturated flow in soils

Soil moisture measurement, monitoring and forecasting

Remote sensing of rainfall, soil type, soil moisture and surface water

Movement of chemicals in soils

10.9.4.2.   Irrigated agriculture

Remote sensing of plant condition

Use of saline water for irrigation

Use of sewage effluent for irrigation

Use of drainage water for irrigation

Further development of groundwater and groundwater recharge

Water/yield relationship

Reduction of crop evapotranspiration

Reduction of open surface evaporation

Use of large level basins

10.9.4.3.   Design

Low energy travelling sprinklers

Trickle irrigation emitters

Low-cost 'intermediate technology' irrigation systems

Low head pipe distribution systems

Low head drop structures

Low head pumps

Silt selective intakes

Automation of in-field control gates and valves

Automation of canal control gates

Remote monitoring and control of canal control gates

Computer simulation of canal operation in on-demand systems

Storage of local run-off for irrigation

Drainage by tube well

Drainage filter materials

Drainage of saline clay soils

Mole drainage of irrigated soils

Computer software for design

Optimisation of geometry and slope of stable channels in alluvium

10.9.4.4.   Construction and maintenance

Guidance systems for land-levelling and construction of field channels, canals and pipelines

Maintenance of canals: desilting; mechanical weed control; biological weed control

Pipelaying machines and pipe materials

Development of GRC and GRP on site pre-casting techniques

10.9.4.5.   Management

Computerised management information systems

Computerised scheduling of irrigation

10.9.5.   Waterways

10.9.5.1.   Hydrology and water control

Effects of impounding tidal waterways

Telemetry and remote-controlled methods for water level monitoring and control

Research into hydrological resources and effects of changes to demand, catchment areas, afforestation, pavings and so on

Flow over flood plains and interaction of flood plains and river channels

Leak detection in canal banks

Floods and droughts: prediction, warning, storage and mitigation

Aquifer development to replenish dry rivers

Pumping stations and associated plant

Sediment movement of fine and coarse material and their mixtures

10.9.5.2.   Dredging and siltation

Dredging: development and evaluation of alternative methods

Prevention and clearance of siltation in channels and locks, including investigation of fluvial and tidal silt movement in rivers

Methods of preventing saline intrusion

10.9.5.3.   Bank and bed protection and lining

Evaluation of water-tight linings, particularly long term

Investigation of bank and bed erosion by fluvial and tidal currents and by craft wash

Revetments, and bank and bed protection

Weed control and cutting

Use of geotextile reinforced vegetative bank protection

10.9.5.4.   Craft and navigation

Optimum shape and dimensions for craft

Optimum channel cross-sections, including turning and passing bays

Movement of craft in restricted channels and openings

Craft operation; supervision and control; codes of practice

Development of commercial craft and cargo handling systems

10.9.5.5.   Bridges and aqueducts

Code of practice for concrete waterway structures

Loading attributable to craft, e.g. impact, suction, erosion

Assessment of old brick and masonry structures and techniques for in situ repairs

Evaluate methods or lining and/or waterproofing aqueduct troughs

Power assistance for swing bridges

10.9.5.6. Locks

Review of locks and other lifting devices to meet future UK requirements (including operation in cold weather)

Methods of reducing tidal in-flow through locks

Detection of voids behind lock walls

Power assistance to lock gates

Methods of arresting craft in locks

10.9.5.7. Tunnels, culverts, channels and geotechnical matters

Methods of assessment and repair/rehabilitation of old brick-lined tunnels (including raising roof in subsidence areas)

Methods of assessment and repair/rehabilitation of culverts under waterways

Methods for investigation of and improving the stability of canal banks and embankments

Soil survey methods relative to the retention of wetlands

10.9.5.8. Other matters

Intermodal transfer requirements at ports and inland centres: loading and packaging systems

Provision for dealing with emergencies

Flexible dam systems

Economic assessment and analysis of proposed waterway projects and maintenance

Standards for the protective coating of plant and craft

Improved use of meteorological information: correlation of numerical models with forecasting and actual experience

10.9.6. Waste disposal

Reference should be made to the text in Section 10.7.

10.9.7. Land reclamation

Reference should be made to the text in Section 10.8.

11. CONSTRUCTION MANAGEMENT, PROCESSES AND SAFETY

11.1. Introduction

The boundaries between science, applied science and engineering are inevitably blurred and indistinct. Civil engineering practice is, however, generally accepted to be a complex mixture of craft knowledge and applied science. Civil engineering research by contrast is largely viewed as applied physics; work is almost entirely centred upon the behaviour of physical systems. In the past, this research emphasis has been entirely justifiable, because without an adequate understanding of the behaviour of physical systems, little progress can be made.

For the purpose of this discussion, the problems facing an engineer in tackling a new project can be divided roughly into two parts: the technical problems of ensuring that the physical system will satisfy the required criteria; and the organisational problems associated with getting the work done. The problems which dominate the work of many engineers are of the organisational kind; further, those are the very problems with which they may feel least able to cope. A study by the University of Bradford for the ICE's Engineering Management Group Board has demonstrated the need felt by civil engineers for better management training. The number of enquiries for the new Diploma in Engineering Management of the major engineering institutions is another manifestation of this need.

While it must be admitted that it is easier to secure dependable theories for physical systems than it is for systems involving human beings, it is the purpose of this Chapter to argue that significant contributions to the organisational problems can be made by suitable research. The methodology for such research will owe much more to social science techniques than to the techniques of the applied physicist. As there is virtually no tradition for such work in civil engineering, there will be a need to attract other professionals into the work. The recent SERC specially promoted programme of research into construction management has recognised the need and is beginning this process. The recognition of the role of human frailty in engineering accidents and the role of social science, defined by Popper as 'the study of the unintended consequences of human action', is another area of developing research. However, it must be expected that progress will be slow and of uneven quality at first because of the major obstacles that have to be overcome before successful interdisciplinary research can be carried out.

In this Chapter, major trends and problems in this area of work are identified. It is not the purpose always to translate these problems into specific research proposals. Work must continue and expand from its present small base to various levels of applicability. For example, at one end of the spectrum, research into developing better cost estimating techniques for a particular organisation might be immediately applicable. At the other end of the spectrum, fundamental research into such basic concepts as risk, responsibility and the role of regulations in design may not seem to be immediately applicable but would provide an intellectual climate for the better propagation of research into organisational systems. Work of this latter type is developing, as exemplified by the new journal 'Civil Engineering Systems' which is specifically aimed at the growing number of researchers who wish to exchange papers on the systems analysis of a broad range of civil engineering topics.

11.2. **Overview of trends**

A consequence of the tight economic climate is the present very close examination of all expenditure. This seems to be resulting in a much greater interest, on the part of all decision makers, in ensuring value for money. This means, in turn, that there is greater interest in control procedures for capital investment programmes, in ensuring an efficient use of resources, in controlling costs and in quality of work.

It is particularly interesting, therefore, that within this climate the recent NEDO Report has argued that the level of Research and Development in the construction industry is far too low, particularly when compared with that of other industries in the UK. It can be argued that this is the first matter that needs to be researched. There is no doubt that the construction industry has a number of characteristics which make it somewhat different from the manufacturing industries. The most significant, as far as research is concerned, is that the product development phase in manufacturing is not present in the design and construction of one-off construction projects. This has meant that there is no natural investment in R&D. This, coupled with the fact that design and construction are usually quite separate and that the client is very often Government, has ensured that many firms in the construction industry do not formally participate in R&D at all, while arguing strongly that R&D is the responsibility of Government. These attitudes and characteristics of the industry have meant that it is difficult to co-ordinate and control research expenditure. In turn, this has resulted in a low perception by many of the value of research.

No one can deny the contribution which research has made towards our understanding of the behaviour of physical systems. As far as the construction industry is concerned, a reason for the low investment in research may be that the leaders of the industry do not see traditional research as being particularly relevant to the industry's current major problems. If these problems are largely organisational then it is possible to understand why. Alternatively, it may be that dissemination of research results is so poor that there are major misunderstandings with regard to research achievements. Clearly, the contractors who have R&D laboratories and the consultants who have R&D departments realise the benefits of some in-house R&D effort to provide a competitive commercial edge. However, there is perhaps too little concept of pre-competitive research, the sort of research which might provide mutual benefits for UK contractors and provide a competitive edge for the UK as a whole over foreign companies. It has not been possible within the scope of this Report to determine the reasons for the low research expenditure, but whatever these reasons are the problem is an organisational one and can be researched using social science methodologies.

Another trend which requires urgent research attention is the quantity of litigation in the construction industry, which does not benefit anyone except the lawyers. The relationship between technology and the law is important at many levels, from the details of the wording of contracts to the expectations of lawyers about the possible performance of engineers under the headings of 'duty of care' and 'fitness for purpose'. The ICE's Legal Affairs Group has commented that some general legal principles and procedures are unhelpful to successful construction, and that engineers, through the Institution, should take a positive attitude towards influencing developments of the law. There is a need to develop a research tradition of critical discussion between lawyers and engineers, particularly in the universities. This should lead to interdisplinary research work which could be of direct benefit to the industry.

It is increasingly being realised that the client's perception of the nature of the industry is not always as good as it ought to be for the best interest of all involved, including the client himself. Value for money is not always obtained by the acceptance of the lowest tender, even from a selected list of contractors. Competitive quoting by consultants can result in the need to cut corners in design work if the fees are too tight. If the designer has no involvement on site, then mistakes can easily occur regarding the importance of some of the technical assumptions. Clients are usually not single individuals with a single mind but are large organisations with their own problems. It is becoming increasingly clear that the interface between client and industry does require research attention.

The role of the new information technologies in the construction industry is an obvious area for research work. The SERC is already exploring the potential for expert systems. As the construction industry has to pass information through many interfaces and as the problems of controlling resources, costs, quality of work and risk are all sensitive to information handling, then the role of these new technologies will be crucial in the future. It is important, however, to learn the lessons of history and not expect too much too soon from an emerging technology. There is much deep thought and work required from the user end of these technologies before they become as effective as they could be; it will not be purely a question of accepting computer systems as handed over by computer scientists; research work must again be of the interdisciplinary kind. For example, knowledge acquisition for expert systems will require input from methods of social science, and uncertainty analysis from applied mathematicion and logicians as well as from computer scientists.

One reviewer of the Task Force papers concluded his comments with the plea, 'Why does everything seem to take longer these days?!' While the despairing note of this remark could be attributed to a number of reasons, it possibly does relate directly to the issue of the organisation and management of civil engineering. It may be argued that it is rather more important to educate and train engineers in already established management skills than to research organisational and human problems in specific contexts. However, that argument does not recognise sufficiently that research is an essential pre-requisite for teaching, in the continuing process of the development of knowledge.

11.3.   Trends in project management

Many of the major industrial employers are now appointing a Project Manager and are dispensing with the Engineer. This is a trend being followed in multidisciplinary projects on a world-wide basis. There is therefore a need for the clarification and simplification of project management procedures. The traditional roles of client, consultant and contractor are frequently changed with the development and increasing use of design and build, turnkey and management contracts. A flexible set of contract conditions, including alternative clauses, may be needed to encompass a wide band of contract strategies now in use, and to enable a more sensible sharing of risk.

Public accountability often demands that the lowest tenders from a selected list be chosen. This many lead to an inadequate consideration of maintenance problems and costs. With an increasing tendency to look at problems as a whole (the so-called 'systems view') there is an increasing realisation that life cycle costing is important and that the uncertain costs of inspection maintenance and repair must be considered. The increasing length of tender lists may in the short term seem to provide the client with greater choice, but in the long term may not be in the client's best interests. Clients are rarely single individuals and hence the attitude and performance of a client, particularly one who has infrequent contact with the construction industry, is an organisational problem. The client's view of financial and technical risks and how they are to be shared, the responsibilities of client and customer, the problems of coping with changes of requirements, and the problems of information flow between all of the parties involved in a project, are all examples of problems that may be helped by suitable research.

Failure to meet time or cost targets on projects is well advertised and applies to both home and overseas jobs. Poor performance is frequently due to the acceptance of unrealistic estimates and ignorance or neglect of risks. The estimating problem is compounded as firms are involved with far bigger jobs, and with continuing and varying levels of inflation. There is a need for operational estimating techniques with proper consideration of the uncertainties involved.

The control of change and uncertainty on contracts, particularly with respect to the burdensome number of claims, is a continuing problem, mainly on UK contracts. There is a need for rational and systematic methods of claims assessment. This may require further development of method related bills of quantities and, more radically, the joint use by client and contractors of some cost-modelling techniques. The increasing dominance of time-related costs means that financial planning cannot be totally delegated to quantity surveyors.

These problems are directly related to the proper control of progress and costs of work. The role of the new information technologies in the processes will be important. Costs and progress are but one aspect of information transfer. The construction industry is characterised by the number of parties involved on a project and the transfer of all information between those parties is crucial to the successful control of the project.

Another area of increasing concern is that of ensuring adequate quality of work. Quality assurance (QA) is a term which already is beginning to mean many different things to different people. It may vary from a simple and specific requirement for the way in which quality of work is to meet the quality of standards defined in the specifications, to a totally general treatment which could involve complex safety analysis and environmental impact analysis which after all are aspects of the quality of the final product. QA applies to design as well as site work. Again, one of the special characteristics of the construction industry is that teams of workers are built up and then run down again over comparatively short time-scales, and at the same time the necessary team attitudes and communications procedures have to be developed. This is true both during design where the client's representatives and a number of professional practices may be involved, and during construction when a large number of subcontractors may be added.

Some people are claiming that QA policies have added considerably to costs without sufficient benefit. Research which examines current experience with some costs against benefit analysis is urgently required. The initiative for QA has come from the nuclear and other power projects, and from offshore and process plant structures. The new Project Management Forum involving other professional engineers will enable open discussion on these and other matters, but the measures of costs and gains in reliability, safety, etc., may be controversial unless backed up by some independent assessments.

The inculcation of 'systems' view, or an overview, on the part of the engineers involved in a project, as well as an ability to deal with detail, is perhaps more a function of education and training than of research. However, there are manifestations of the lack of this overview in project control. For example site investigations are often skimped to reduce apparent or budgeted first costs and there are often severe later cost penalties. Maintenance and inspection needs are not adequately considered; designing for demolition is almost unheard of. An awareness of these issues is growing and research is required on the best ways of developing these attitudes in educational training. A greater use of management games in civil engineering may be one solution, and a high priority should be given to their development.

While education and training in civil engineering has received a great deal of attention in recent years, the building industry is only just emerging from an attitude that to have a degree is to be overqualified. The construction industry as a whole has a 'low tech' image which stems largely from building. Civil engineering companies require high standards of educational achievement from their graduates but often cannot reward them sufficiently to prevent the 'high flyers' from moving to more highly paid professions.

The merging of the Institution of Municipal Engineers with the Institution of Civil Engineers is a hopeful indication that the historical trend of the divergence of professional groups within UK industry is waning in the construction industry, and this may go some way to enabling a greater appreciation of the importance of overview. The development of mandating CPD and the Diploma in Engineering Management is encouraging.

There is an increasing shortage of skilled craftsmen with the necessary 'folk knowledge', which the old style foreman had, which would enable them to correct, where necessary, the inbuilt assumptions of designers. Building labour is increasingly not indigenous and the apprenticeship system appears to be breaking down. Because of this, several commentators are surprised that there seems to be no clear trend towards increasing the amount of work done off site. The reasons may be difficulties in the logistics of transportation and handling, and the relationship between design work and site work.

Overseas work needs to be approached with a proper knowledge of local conditions and an appropriate use of indigenous resources. British contractors have often chosen a capital intensive route. Priorities in the appropriate use of technology are twofold. Firstly, there is a need for the development of methods of assessment of ongoing construction projects in low income countries, not only in technical and economic terms but also taking account of their impact on the societies for whose needs they were designed. Secondly, methods need to be developed for the communication of the results of R&D relevant to low income countries to those who could make use of such information in improving the planning, design and execution of future projects.

11.4. Trends in construction processes

The capability to design and produce construction plant in the UK has diminished progressively with the shrinking UK construction market.

The situation currently faced by construction plant manufacturers is by no means unique to their industry and tends to reflect back to the days of buoyant home markets when an overseas market was not necessary for profitability, let alone for survival.

Many UK companies have been slow to see the need for developing equipment for varying needs in different areas of world construction. As a result, they are now faced with established organisations selling well-tried and accepted equipment on a world market. Even when the right product is there for sale there are already too many world-wide plant manufacturers producing too much almost identical equipment at fiercely competitive prices. It is therefore inevitable that many companies must either cease trading, amalgamate interest or diversify into new products.

There are three categories of construction equipment which need to be considered.

- The first group comprises large, highly productive machines, such as earth-moving equipment, which either reduce unit production costs or stabilise them with a higher output capacity. However, since markets need to be assured to justify large initial capital investment, it is difficult to see how any such major new construction equipment can be produced in this country except as an extension to an existing product range selling to a widely established world market, or by manufacture under licence from others.

- The second category comprises mid-range jobbing machines which are owned by most contractors or available readily from hire fleets. The main requirements for such machines are robustness, reliability, simplicity of operation and maintenance, and a relatively cheap capital cost coupled with the ability to perform adequately over a long life. This category is the most prolific and covers medium-sized hydraulic excavators and shovels, forklifts, rollers, compressors, dumpers, hoists, etc. It is also the most competitive for the plant manufacturers, and largely covers the needs of developing countries as well as providing UK stock production.

- The third category comprises the small plant and equipment at the bottom of the range, probably representing the largest growth potential with the greatest scope for design ingenuity with the lowest capital investment. This group comprises materials handling equipment and access equipment of every description, together with hand tools, formwork and so on.

The four components of construction costs are labour, plant, materials and overheads. The relationship between them varies with the type of work and relative costs. Changes in the proportions can lead to overall cost savings. For example, an increase in the proportion attributable to plant might not only save on labour but also, by saving time, reduce overheads. It follows then that a reduction in plant costs by improved productivity or the use of more economic plant will produce benefits. The general design approach of minimising the material content of construction projects may not allow the best or economic use of plant and equipment. As mentioned in Section 11.3, the problems of design and construction need to be veiwed 'as a whole' using a 'systems' approach.

The criteria for the effectiveness of plant are different in developing and developed countries. In developing countries, the criteria include lowest capital cost, robustness to poor operators, ease of maintenance, wide variety of site utilisation and suitability for use by unskilled operators. In the developed countries, the criteria include lowest operating costs, reliability, ease of maintenance, high utilisation, minimisation of labour operations and conformity with best environmental standards. The design and manufacture of plant is no longer the sole prerogative of the developed countries. The scale of world-wide demand is influenced by the increasing use of construction plant in the developing areas with the emphasis on simple, rugged machines. These large markets can influence the economics of production costs and enable selling prices to be viewed for political and national purposes. The competitive pressures on contractors and plant manufacturers result in the emphasis on plant development being an improved cost effectiveness. This is sought by improving durability of components, versatility to enhance useful applications, and ease of maintenance.

The future needs of labour in the construction industry are likely to be as follows:

- devices to eliminate the physical effort involved in lifting, moving, pulling or breaking
- equipment to eliminate or minimise the effect of weather on construction projects
- mechanisation to increase safety and reduce health hazards
- equipment to reduce the possibility of human error
- equipment to eliminate the drudgery of routine work
- integration of site handling systems to give compatibility and simple interchange.

The equipment used is, however, largely dictated by the design of the particular project; closer liaison between designers, contractors and plant manufacturers can only eventually benefit all three.

The construction site needs to be examined to determine the extent of possible off-site manufacture, the pre-planned use of plant and other resources, and the rapid site assembly of the off-site manufactured components. Labour-intensive work is becoming increasingly expensive in UK construction and this problem needs attention. The need to provide a safe place to work and methods of work which are acceptable in terms of noise, fumes, dust, etc., is the result of recent legislation and has resulted in some re-examination of methods.

There has, however, been very little research attention given to the identification of the factors which are likely to influence the development and use of construction plant in the next twenty years or so. R&D in the construction plant industry is evolving from competitive commercial pressure with little sign of an overall strategy. There is a need for studies on the better use of plant and equipment on site to reduce material waste. The increased use of management contracting in building provides the potential for better integration of the design of permanent works with site processes.

It is essential that an ongoing dialogue between designers, builders and plant manufacturers develops, to facilitate the introduction of new potential construction technology into initial design concepts. It is important that material suppliers, builders and plant manufacturers, together with those responsible for initial specifications, realise the importance of proper packaging and handling of materials.

The interest of each member in the chain must be towards the cost of the product when placed and paid for. Both suppliers and builders need to understand that the cheapest bought product, unless received in the right form and handled in the correct manner, can cost most when installed.

There is also a need for discussion and liaison between the manufacturers of materials handling equipment. It is, for instance, no good making a hoist if material packages cannot be placed in it by a forklift, or there is no simple way of moving such materials out of a hoist to the work place. This is just one example where integration of systems between manufacturers is desirable. There is no one company that produces such an integrated system where all the problems are recognised.

One of the notable growth markets is in refurbishment and repair works. Much of this could be improved if special purpose-designed equipment were available instead of modified standard equipment. The recycling of waste products and once used products can provide commercial advantages in some circumstances. This is a challenge to be met in materials technology and in the design of new plant to make recycling processes possible.

Appreciable development has occurred in the use of microcomputers for plant control and this will continue. One of the most urgent areas for research work is the use of robotics and automation in construction. It requires a wide-ranging approach with perhaps the funding of a large number of small ingenious projects, initially to develop ideas. It has been suggested that the UK is already a long way behind Japan in this area.

Surveying has traditionally been viewed as a low technology. Modern developments in microprocessors are changing surveying equipment dramatically. There is vast potential for improving current procedures used for maintenance and repair operations, and a wide market for improved setting out techniques, not only for the more traditional kind of civil engineering structure but also for the more complex type built in relatively hostile environments. Remote sensing has had some research support in the UK, but it needs more. The impact of the new space technology is likely to revolutionise both the concepts and procedures of engineering surveying as they are practised today. Theodolites, levels and control networks may all disappear in about 15 to 20 years. Other developments in terrestrial instrumentation (e.g. remote monitoring systems or laser EDMS which require no reflectors) may introduce changes much earlier in the procedures used for monitoring structural deformations or for the verification of design shapes (e.g. dams, cooling towers, etc.).

Automatic data acquisition will be possible for many more circumstances than is currently the case. Much research will be needed for the analysis of these data. These analyses will provide information for the control and management of the performance of structures and the determination of other types of inspection and maintenance procedures. The analyses will have to be relevant to the interpretation of imprecise and uncertain data as, for example, in the interpretation of borehole logs. Electronic data transmission and methods of communication, such as Ceefax and Contra Vision, will affect site practice.

Quality assurance (QA) has been discussed in Section 11.3. Accurate, rapid and reliable methods are required to control both on-site and off-site production of concrete and bituminous materials, to check the relevant qualities of materials such as timber, steel aggregate and cement, and to assess the quality being achieved on site. A number of concrete batching plants can now provide a print-out of the materials used in each batch which can be used as part of a QA system. Steel fabricators, led by BCSA, are implementing QA systems. The use of weather protection systems is not growing as might be expected. There is a need for a better and consistent working environment in order to ensure quality of construction.

11.5.   Safety

Risk analysis and quality assurance are inevitably bound up with the analysis of uncertainty and the role of humans in complex socio-technical systems. This is an area where very little research has been done and where a large amount of research effort is required, particularly for socio-technical systems with high consequent but low chance of failure.

Shortly after its formation in 1978, the Construction Industry Advisory Committee (CONIAC) set up a working party to examine research into the safety of individuals on construction sites. In 1979, it published a report which generally concluded that although a considerable amount of research and development work was being carried out in the construction field, very little had been directed at improving safety performance on construction sites.

It was therefore decided to produce a second report (not yet published) which would list current construction health and safety research and also provide ideas for future projects. The aim was to provide a guide to existing projects and to stimulate future activities by research bodies, academic institutions and industry. If funding were not available for what CONIAC considered to be very promising areas of research, then they would try to obtain financial support. Whether such support were available or not, promising proposals would be included in the register.

In September 1985, a survey of 137 parties was undertaken (including universities and polytechnics, professional bodies, government departments, trade unions, local authority associations, major client bodies and training organisations). Thirty-six responses were received, and these revealed that very little research or development work was being directed at improving health and safety of performance.

Faced with worsening accident figures for fatal and major injuries and the limited amount of research aimed at improving the situation, CONIAC considered that if improvements were to be obtained, research should be targeted at known high risk activities, e.g. steel erection, demolition, roof work and maintenance operations associated with all types of buildings and structures.

Statistics show that construction is four times more dangerous than manufacturing industry as a whole, with an average of about 150 killed and nearly 2000 suffering major injuries each year on site. Efforts by the Health and Safety Executive, FCEC, BEC and others to improve this record have had little effect to date. In 1985, the Presidents of the Institutions of Civil and Structural Engineers asked the Standing Committee on Structural Safety, chaired by Sir Derman Christopherson, to investigate the problem and to advise them on what research or other action is required to ensure greater safety on site.

The Standing Committee is due to report before the end of 1986 and its report, together with the results of discussions by the ICE's Safety Committee, will need to be taken into account when reviewing priorities for R&D on the subject.

11.6. Research needs

The highest priority items identified in this review are given in italics, but the relative priorities of other items will occasionally require re-assessment.

The following list is not exhaustive and really consists of a list of problems of varying levels of generality. The lack of precision in the definition of some of the problems is inevitable as research on these topics is not well established and there is a need for general exploratory work before detailed proposals can be made. There is an urgent need to establish a community of researchers interested in these problems and they should give urgent attention to their research methodology. A start has been made with the SERC's specially promoted programme in construction management.

11.6.1. General

To investigate why investment into research for the construction industry seems to be lower than in other industries; if research seems to be undervalued by the industry to find the reasons

To investigate how best to close the gap between what is known and what is applied; to investigate the communication of R&D information between industry, research institutes, universities and government departments

To investigate the proper identification of problems in the management and control of jobs so that drawings, specifications, etc., are used for creative functions rather than for fiscal, defensive purposes; to explore why the reality of the site is often so different from the precision of design assumptions

To investigate the relationship of construction with construction law and to determine whether any of the general legal principles and procedures are unhelpful to successful construction; to investigate the reasons for the increased litigation in the industry; to consider the expectations of lawyers regarding the industry and the relationship of basic terms such as 'duty of care' and 'fitness for purpose' to the philosophy of knowledge

To investigate the role of regulations, codes of practice and other legal constraints upon successful design and construction

To investigate the nature of risk in the construction industry and its relationship with responsibility and legal requirements; to investigate the appropriateness of quantitative risk analysis and the modellings of uncertain knowledge; to investigate ways of using case study material as a basis for the control of future projects

To investigate the need for and the nature of environmental impact analysis; to investigate the appropriateness of quantitative methods and the modellings of uncertain knowledge

To investigate, in a wide-ranging study to generate ideas, the potential for the imaginative use of information technology in the construction industry; to investigate how it can be used to improve communications within the industry; to recommend possible application areas for expert systems and robotics and automation including the control of quality, costs, risks, inspection and maintenance; to investigate ways of establishing public data bases

To investigate the role of the client in the construction industry; to consider the client as an organisation and its interaction with the design/ construction organisations; to examine ways in which the client may obtain best value for money which take proper account of maintenance costs and other factors which may not be adequately considered in the acceptance of the lowest tender; to consider the unintended consequences of competitive tendering for design work; to investigate whether a significant number of clients do not sufficiently understand the risks involved in a project and whether they have unrealistic expectations of the construction industry; to devise procedures for the long-term maintenance of a structure after contract completion by properly trained staff

To investigate the appropriateness of management training for civil engineers and other professionals in the construction industry; to examine, for teaching purposes, the relationship between decision making in design and in management and the need for students to be exposed to both open and closed form problems; to investigate the role of management games in undergraduate teaching

To investigate how best to assist the development of indigenous construction industries in low income countries with an appropriate involvement of UK companies

To develop methods for the assessment of ongoing construction projects in low income countries not only in technical and economic terms but also in terms of the impact on the society for whose needs they were designed; to develop methods for the dissemination of appropriate R&D information and to focus attention on the need to enhance local production, using local resources and technologies which can be established and maintained while recognising the aspirations of people and politicians

11.6.2. Project management

To carry out a fundamental review of contract strategies needed; to investigate the possibility of providing a flexible set of contract conditions for varying circumstances which would enable a more sensible sharing of risk; to develop model conditions of contract for management contracting and to consider the need for special contract conditions for projects involving appropriate technology for low income countries

To investigate the relationship of legal liability with the insurance industry and to consider possible alternatives to the present system

To investigate tendering and contract procedures, the design team organisation and the two-stage tendering procedures, so that the general contractor may be involved in the development of the final design

To investigate better techniques for the control of financial risk; to develop better methods for cost estimating and bidding strategies; to consider the role of decision analysis techniques and quantitative risk analysis

To develop methods of uncertainty analysis which cater for imprecise, possibly inconsistent data; these methods would be applied to project control of risk, quality, costs and to the more detailed problems such as the interpretation of borehole data

To assess the current effectiveness of QA procedures; to study case histories or projects where QA has been applied and to determine costs and benefits; to examine QA in its broadest sense which includes safety, cost, environmental impact analyses; to investigate the effectiveness of QA at a detailed level for concrete and bituminious products, and to examine how the chances of occurrence of problems such as alkali silica reaction in concrete can be minimised in future projects

To investigate the effectiveness of the roles of the Project Manager and the Engineer

To investigate the effectiveness of current procedures with respect to the maintenance and inspection of structures; to develop the concept of life-cycle costing and to develop better methods for the realistic comparison of costs and benefits

To investigate the methods of artificial intelligence in project control; this will include the development of expert systems and 'intelligent' knowledge bases for risk analysis, quality assurance, cost control, designing inspection and maintenance programs

To investigate the role of communication networks, which can link groups of individuals by sound and vision and which can transmit hard copies of information in the control of project information

To develop computer systems for project control to be used by small builders

To develop a computerised link between bills of quantities and specifications, and to investigate the possibilities of standardised specifications

To develop rational and systematic methods for coping with changes in requirements; to develop methods of claims assessments possibly based

on method related bills of quantity and the joint use of some cost modelling techniques

To investigate ways in which wastage of materials can be minimised on site; likewise, better control of toxic substances is required

To investigate the effects of recent changes in site industrial relations procedures which are reported to have resulted in less productivity; to examine the procedures the CEGB has taken to alleviate the problem

To investigate the current availability of labour and to examine the reasons for a shortage of skilled craftsmen; to study the apparent breakdown of the apprenticeship system

To investigate the ownership and control of waterways with a view to the best use of resources, resolving conflicts of interest and optimising engineering works

To investigate the ways in which energy can be conserved on site by appropriate management; to study how energy can be conserved in the production of basic construction materials

11.6.3. *Construction processes*	*To investigate the factors which are likely to influence the development and use of construction plant in the next 20 years or so*

To examine and develop the formal role of terotechnology; this is the specification, design, provision, installation, maintenance, modification and replacement of plant machinery, equipment, buildings and structures with the feedback of information on performance, design and costs. Its objective is a combination of engineering management, financial and other practices applied to physical assets in pursuit of life cycle costs

To examine the problems concerned with the demolition of structures, particularly complex ones; to explore the reasons why eventual demolition is rarely considered in the design of a structure even if it is anticipated that the structure will have only one owner

To examine the role of robotics and automation in construction plant; to generate, in a free-ranging study, ideas for possible future developments; to follow up developments in the applications of robotics to tunnelling machines, offshore inspection and brick-laying machines

To investigate the potential for more off-site manufacture of components to be assembled on site

To investigate possible applications for the developments in modern surveying techniques — for example, to investigate the potential for deformation monitoring of structures using remote sensing techniques; to examine the implications for general site practice from the developments in surveying equipment and techniques; to develop methods of analysis which can deal with the potentially large volumes of uncertain data at varying levels of precision of definition — these methods will be developments of time series analysis and uncertainty techniques for knowledge engineering

To develop remote-controlled scraper and grading units; to develop machines that can spread and compact to level, filling and sub-bases

To develop alternatives for current formwork designs

To develop machines for pipe laying without trenching; there is also an apparent urgent need for machines capable of excavating the pipe laying, adding concrete surround and backfilling as the machine proceeds

To develop better weather protection systems for site constructions

To develop the use of water jets, particularly for rock cutting and rock breaking tools

To consider the need for construction plant which can operate on difficult land with low bearing capacity

To consider the usage of water for site processes, such as aggregate cleaning, in countries where uncontaminated water is in short supply

To determine whether small hand tools need developing in order to improve the effectiveness of artisans

To develop special purpose-designed equipment for refurbishment and repair work

11.6.4. Safety

To investigate the nature of human error in socio-technical systems and to develop management procedures which will enable the better control of safety and risk both to civil engineering structures and to site personnel

To investigate the role of prototype testing and proof load testing in controlling the safety of civil engineering structures

To investigate methods of assessing the safety of damaged structures (damaged by explosions, earthquakes, etc.)

To develop an expert computer system for planning for safety aspects and hazards of construction activities

To develop and evaluate management procedures, based upon known techniques for changing work behaviour, in order to improve safety on construction sites

To establish the range and nature of the practical consequences for safety which can arise from the use of sub-contractors

To investigate the average cost of a reportable accident; to show that it is possible to save money by reducing the number of accidents; to establish whether there is a firm correlation between productivity and accident prevention by good management

To obtain more detailed information on the exposure of workers to construction site noise; to carry out a feasibility study into setting up an audiometric testing programme; to identify the primary cause(s) for failure in control of noise exposure

To undertake a study and produce guidance on the safe use of explosives for underwater demolition

To investigate whether the form and means of transmission of construction safety information is appropriate and whether such information is reaching the intended recipients.

12. PRIORITIES IN RESEARCH AND DEVELOPMENT

12.1. Introduction

In making its review of R&D requirements, the Task Force thought mainly in terms of the product and market areas, partly because the requirements are more readily identified in terms of their application, but also because of the strongly held view that practitioner users of R&D results should take the lead in establishing R&D requirements and priorities. In Chapters 4–11, this present review has followed a similar path to that of the Task Force. However, because R&D is usually conducted on a discipline basis, it is convenient — as the Task Force found — to present recommendations on that basis.

In order to highlight the effects of changes and events that have occurred since the Task Force Report was issued in 1981, the same seven discipline headings are adopted in this Chapter as in the Task Force Report. Under each heading, the appropriate extract from the Task Force Report is given together with a commentary expressing additions and changes, including changes in emphasis now necessary as a result of this present review summarised in Chapters 4–11.

It is recognised that civil engineering design and construction needs to draw on a broad spectrum of disciplines in many of its activities. The Task Force Report involved 28 different disciplines, in addition to the basic sciences of mathematics, physics and chemistry. In many cases, the R&D required needs to be interdisciplinary but, usually, the main thrust of the work will fall within one or another of the seven discipline headings given in this Chapter.

This Chapter is necessarily only a summary and it must be emphasised that, in framing programmes and priorities for R&D, the individual market areas given in Chapters 4–11 should be studied in detail.

12.2. Assembly of physical data

12.2.1. Extract from Task Force Report

The planning stage is of vital importance to the success of a major civil engineering project. It includes interpreting, or often establishing, the client's requirements, comparing alternative solutions, preparing a detailed design brief and presenting information for evaluation and approval by the client and other interested parties. It requires the acquisition and synthesis of data and other information on, for example, political, sociological, economic and ecological influences bearing on the project; information on the site topography, geology, hydrology and climate; information on human, material and financial resources available. It also requires methods of analysing and interpreting existing data or rapid methods of obtaining specific data.

One important and continuing requirement, therefore, is for national organisations such as the Institute of Geological Sciences and other agencies of the Natural Environment Research Council, Institute of Hydrology, Meteorological Office, Ordnance Survey, Department of the Environment and others, to maintain and better co-ordinate an effective information service and, particularly, to expand the information available from overseas.

There is a strong need for the development of 'intelligent' instruments for site survey and investigation, with automatic data processing and presentation, and positioning devices and of inertial surveying. Better techniques and equipment are needed for exploration and exploitation of the oceans.

More reliable methods are required to interpret data of various kinds to predict, for example, wave and wind characteristics, rainfall and run-off, ground conditions, seismic effects etc., particularly for work overseas and in unfamiliar or adverse climates.

Risk assessment and evaluation, including the effects of environmental impact, are other aspects of the planning stage requiring considerable development with regard to data collection, methods of analysis and understanding of perceived risk. Economic and technical assessment of completed schemes is essential to success in planning new ones.

Another high priority area is the development and use of computer methods for application to management and control of the whole construction process, from planning to completion.

12.2.2. *Commentary*

The present review is broadly in accord with the Task Force's recommendations on requirements for the assembly of physical data but with some additions and changes in emphasis.

The requirement for more reliable methods to interpret data of various kinds is strongly supported but the establishment and maintenance of reliable data is itself an important requirement, such as, for example, in infrastructure condition monitoring, traffic forecasting to incorporate the effects of congestion and new infrastructures, and in assessing water quality objectives.

Recent events have highlighted the need for improved methods of risk assessment and better understanding of perceived risk in relation to the safety of nuclear power and the storage or disposal of nuclear waste. Risk evaluation, including the effects of environmental impact, is similarly of considerable importance, particularly with regard to new approaches to inner city reclamation and development, urban surface water drainage and overflows from combined sewers.

The rapid growth of interest in the environment and increasing calls for environmental impact analysis represent a major requirement for R&D in connection with most world market areas.

Some other areas requiring the assembly of reliable data and methods of analysis are the interaction between city form, demand for travel and choice of work, also to achieve an optimisation between sewer and treatment works, effluent disposal and water management, sludge disposal and utilisation.

There is complete agreement that economic and technical assessment of completed schemes is essential to success in planning new ones.

12.3. Materials

12.3.1. *Extract from Task Force Report*

Decisions on the selection of materials, required in the planning, design and construction stages of a project, are based on such considerations as conservation, economy, performance, ease of construction and also ease and cost of maintenance. A steady improvement in the quality and use of traditional construction materials during the past 30 years has been accompanied by the introduction of new materials, especially plastics, composites and modified versions of traditional materials, some of which have failed to perform satisfactorily. During the next 20 years or so, economic and conservational pressures will be the main factors influencing the choice of construction materials and the most important R&D requirements are for better methods of test, reliable data on properties and performance, particularly related to durability and cost in use, the development of some new materials for specific purposes and of better protective treatments.

There is considerable need and scope for improved methods of acceptance testing and controlling the qualities of all types of material and for establishing realistic acceptance criteria and limits.

Another important requirement is for reliable data on the long-term behaviour and durability characteristics of new and traditional materials and components under the conditions of exposure they must withstand in practice — for example, in aggressive water and atmosphere, in extremes of temperature and stress. The corrosion of steel and that of steel reinforcement and prestressing tendons are continuing problems requiring solution.

The growing need to use unfamiliar or poorer quality local materials in the UK and overseas, and to make use of recycled and waste materials, gives rise to the requirement for an increased R&D effort in the engineering properties, quality control and use of these materials.

Developments are also required in higher performance coatings for steel, timber, concrete and sealants for joints, together with more reliable and more tolerant methods of applying or renewing them.

12.3.2. Commentary

The present review strongly supports the need for improved methods of acceptance testing and control and for the establishment of realistic criteria, but would add the importance of developing methods to enable the relevant properties and performance of materials and components to be monitored and appraised in service. The probable development of QA procedures and systems will generate substantial R&D requirements in these connections.

Assurance of appropriate durability in service is another important requirement on which reliable data is lacking and there has been a tendency to underestimate the conditions of exposure, particularly in terms of temperature, humidity and aggressive water or septic sewage. A further requirement is that economic methods of repair or replacement must be available.

It is also important that R&D on materials and components should be in step with relevant R&D in design and construction to ensure satisfactory practical application.

12.4. Geotechnics

12.4.1. Extract from Task Force Report

The subject of geotechnics is taken here to comprise soil and rock mechanics, foundation and earthworks design. It has an influence, therefore, on all types of construction and is sometimes the dominating influence, for example, in embankments and underground construction. As a relatively new discipline, geotechnics is still developing rapidly but there are several important gaps, particularly in site investigation and predictive testing and in knowledge of the performance of foundations and interaction between ground and structure.

The development of site investigation techniques and methods of testing (particularly in situ) and interpretation to establish properties of soils and rocks and relevant parameters for design and construction are of prime importance. Improved remote control methods of monitoring deformation, strain and force are required for a variety of earth structures and foundations both during and after construction, including seismic effects.

With overseas work especially in mind, information is required on the behaviour and performance of soils and foundations in non-temperate countries, for example, on tills, residual soils and desiccated or frozen materials and other soils which do not always behave in standard ways. For work in the UK, there is a need to expand the information available on various soil-types and to develop ground treatments and foundations for construction on reclaimed, contaminated or poor ground.

There is also need for work on the behaviour of soils and foundations under repeated loading and under dynamic loading, on the properties of sea bed soils and on the performance of sea bed foundations. A further requirement is for prediction and monitoring of the long term stability of underground constructions.

12.4.2. Commentary

The findings of this present review on geotechnics are closely in agreement with those in the Task Force Report. It further emphasises the continuing need for improved methods of site investigation and testing to provide information of direct use and application in analysis, design and construction. Description, classification and characterisation of rock masses in engineering terms is a further requirement.

Behaviour of soils and soil/structure interaction under cyclic and dynamic, including seismic, loading and to extremes of temperature are other important requirements.

In the UK, it is increasingly important to make good use of poor ground, including reclaimed land and old industrial and under-mined sites. Effective methods need to be developed to assess such sites, to improve bearing capacity and stability and to ensure satisfactory durability and performance of foundations and underground structures.

The use of geotextiles has increased in recent years. Tests conducted on these materials in the absence of soil are of limited value, and the need now is for research into their behaviour in association with various soils, both in the laboratory and in practice.

It is important that a sensible balance should be maintained in future research work in ground engineering. Fundamental work should continue in order to improve our knowledge of the constitutive relationships of soils and rocks and to apply the latest computational techniques in design. However, this present review is in agreement with the Task Force's recommendation that greater benefit is likely to accrue from properly designed large and full-scale tests and from careful monitoring of full-scale works during and after construction.

12.5.   Structures

12.5.1. Extract from Task Force Report

Although further improvements in analytical methods and computer applications will occur during the next 20 years or so, and will be required to deal mainly with complex problems, such as those involving dynamic loads and non-linear effects, the main requirements for the future are to improve the correlation between models and actual structures and to develop the application of existing tools in automated design and drawing.

There is need to establish better data on some aspects of wind loadings, particularly the wind structure over hills or non-uniform terrain and proximity effects of other structures, and to develop wind data for tropical climates to the same level as for temperate climates. For maritime and offshore structures the need is for data on wave and current force spectra. Mainly for work overseas, better information is required on seismic effects. In all these cases, it is necessary to have data on and means of predicting structural response, often including the foundatons and soil.

Data are required on structural interaction between components and parts of buildings before any further major improvement can be made in their structural design and this will require full-scale tests. Similarly, full-scale tests are required to establish the behaviour of joints and some other repetitive design features in order to establish design criteria and standards. Data on the performance of buildings in use are also required to determine serviceability limits, compatibility between components, the effects of design features and other relevant parameters on durability, safety and serviceability. Another need is for studies of performance in use to develop designs for economy and ease of maintenance, repair and alteration.

For overseas work, simplified design procedures and construction methods need to be developed for a range of structures — bridges, culverts, housing, hospitals — suitable for construction with indigenous materials and labour. Specific requirements for work in the UK are likely to include more economical large span buildings, floating structures, aerogenerators and waterproof underground constructions.

12.5.2. *Commentary*	From this present review there is general agreement with the Task Force on the importance of improving the correlation between analytical models and real structures, data on the interaction between components and parts of buildings, the performance of buildings and structures in use and satisfactory means of applying these data in design. The development of designs to achieve economy in use, together with ease of maintenance, repair and alteration, is also a highly important objective.

There is also agreement with the Task Force's recommendation regarding wind, wave and current loadings. However, there is a continuing need also to establish and keep under review other forms of loading, such as traffic on bridges, floor loads on offices, warehouses and retail premises which have all been subject to change in operation or standards over the past decade or two. Impact, seismic and other accidental loadings are also of importance.

Problems with the 'weatherscreen' aspects of buildings of all types open up a further important area of R&D, particularly to improve weather proofing, durability and ease of maintenance and repair of the building envelope and its components and comfort within the building. The R&D required is interdisciplinary, often concerned with interfaces and gaps between the professions and the problems themselves have usually arisen from failure to keep research on materials, design and construction in step and in association.

Events since the Task Force Report was prepared highlight the need for greater attention to R&D on the durability of materials and components of all types, together with cost-effective methods of maintaining, repairing and eventually replacing them. This, together with the market demands for refurbishment and demolition in difficult situations, was not adequately recognised by the Task Force. Another need is to develop expertise in the design of structures subjected to dynamic loading.

Although the Task Force pointed out the need for improvements in information transfer, this present review stresses the importance and urgency for effective action in this field.

12.6.   Hydraulics and public health

12.6.1. *Extract from Task Force Report*	An important need for R&D in hydraulics is for better data, instrumentation and methods of predicting parameters required for design, such as wave current and flow characteristics, sediment transport and scour. Primarily the requirement is for field data either for direct use in design or to correlate with and assess the various mathematical and physical models which have been developed during the past decade or so. Improving the accuracy and confidence levels of wave and current predictions are particularly important to future work offshore in deeper water and also for wave and tidal generators.

Full-scale tests and careful observations on existing installations are required to provide performance data on, for example, coastal protection, drainage, irrigation storage and water supply systems, including low cost systems suitable for work overseas.

Analytical methods are required for complex (e.g. moored) systems involving interaction between dynamic flow and structural response. Pollutant transport and dispersion models are needed for both sewers and open waterways.

It is likely that new types of sewage treatment and waste disposal plants will be required to exploit advances in biotechnology and that design for series of small river hydro-electric schemes, for wave and tide energy production and for offshore structures in deeper waters will place new demands for R&D on hydraulic structures and hydraulic/structure interaction.

In the UK and other developed countries, important requirements are for methods of inspecting, assessing, renovating and replacing existing pipelines and sewers. Improved design and construction techniques are needed for new construction in the UK and overseas. Although new methods of water purification and sewage treatment are likely to develop, there remains the need to improve the efficiency and quality of existing processes and, especially overseas, for better methods of management and operation.

12.6.2. Commentary

The summary of the Task Force's recommendations in this broad area remains appropriate to the finds of this present review, but there are some additional important requirements, particularly in the areas of waste disposal, irrigation, urban drainage and flood control.

For water supply in the UK the main needs are now for maintenance, repair and updating of existing plants and distributive systems. In sewerage and sewage treatment, the trend is towards rehabilitation and maintenance, rather than new work.

Although considerable progress has been made since the Task Force Report on the inspection, renovation and replacement of existing pipelines and sewers, involving 'no-dig' processes, this remains an important requirement for development in the UK and other developed countries.

Waste disposal in the UK and many other highly populated developed countries is a growing problem, particularly concerning landfill sites, requiring R&D to render sites more acceptable from an environmental point of view and safe with regard to water supplies. Research is required on the behaviour of wastes and the mechanics of leachate production and attenuation. The disposal of hazardous, including nuclear wastes, is another area for interdisciplinary research.

Irrigation represents a large market for overseas work, requiring research on the performance of existing schemes and the development of most cost-effective new schemes. It also requires the development of specific pumping and other equipment requiring minimum maintenance and operation skills.

With regard to river management, drought and flood control, the need is for co-ordinated R&D resulting in optimum management of whole river basins, taking into account the effects of changes in water table in both urban and rural areas.

There is a strong need for better instrumentation, hydrological and other data and also for control devices in the whole field of hydraulics and public health both in the UK and overseas.

Improved performance of hydraulic structures is another important objective together with better means of inspecting and monitoring existing structures, particularly dams and reservoirs.

In the field of maritime engineering, the Task Force correctly emphasised the need for better data, instrumentation and methods of predicting parameters required for design. Sediment transport, diffusion from outfalls, performances of breakwaters, groynes and erosion protection schemes are all important R&D areas in coastal engineering. For ports and harbours, the design of quay walls, channel maintenance and ship behaviour in exposed channels and berths are important areas. Tidal energy and wave energy structures present a number of additional problems, particularly in 2D and 3D modelling in complex tidal waters and for improved wave and current data. Tidal power is a particular area where environmental and ecological factors are highly important and where modelling is also a necessary requirement.

12.7. Construction processes

12.7.1. *Extract from Task Force Report*

Accurate, rapid and reliable methods are required to control both on-site and off-site production of concrete and bituminous materials, to check the relevant qualities of materials such as timber, steel, aggregate and cement and to assess the quality of construction being achieved on site. In parallel with the development of robust control testing equipment, which must be capable of use in adverse conditions, it is necessary to establish realistic requirements for the quality of materials and workmanship appropriate to various types of work.

Better methods, equipment and plant are required for: moving, lifting and placing large and very heavy units; sinking large diameter shafts, including those in permeable and saturated strata; tunnelling in mixed faces and variable strata; transport of spoil; rapid welding; compacting embankments and pavements; preparing and protecting exposed surfaces; and for work underwater such as excavating, dredging, drilling and grouting.

The operations of excavating trenches, installing pipes and services, backfilling and reinstatement represent a considerable volume of civil engineering work, both in the UK and overseas. There is a continuing need to improve the methods and equipment for these operations on land and to develop new techniques for work offshore.

The increasing necessity to build in poor quality or fill material requires the development of reliable geotechnical processes, such as compaction, grouting or stabilisation, to improve the quality of the material and in some cases, it will require new forms of foundation, especially when the land is contaminated or aggressive. Geotechnical processes are also required to be developed to improve the properties of the sea bed.

Control systems, based on advances in other technologies, will need to be developed for a wide range of construction plant and for use in both general and specific types of operation. The application of robotics must also be considered, especially for off-site fabrication.

Reappraisal of the influences of design features, materials and components on the quality and economy achieved in construction is required with regard to expected changes in the resources available in the UK and to the efficient use of indigenous materials and labour overseas. Social influences in the UK during the next 20 years are considered likely to have considerable effect on construction processes, requiring greater safety, comfort and weather protection for the workforce and better control over noise and dust pollution.

Development of better transceiver devices for communication on site, better systems of communicating design requirements to site and the provision of systems analysis data would usefully improve the management and control of operations.

12.7.2. *Commentary*

The above summary on construction processes prepared by the Task Force is still relevant today, but more specific objectives now include the introduction of quality assurance and a necessary improvement in safety on the site. The need for development of geotechnical processes and of pipeline repair and replacement has been mentioned in Sections 12.4.2 and 12.6.2.

Advances have taken place in the past 5 years on control systems making use of lasers and microprocessors, but there is a continuing need for advancement in this area. Some progress has been made towards the development of robotics for application both on and off site and this is, again, a potentially important advance.

To achieve revival of the UK plant, industry would require substantial R&D support from the Department of Trade and Industry; it is considered that such support is particularly justified in the area of small plant and equipment for materials handling, access, formwork, hand tools, etc. There is also a strong demand for more robust, reliable mid-range plant that is simpler to operate and maintain. In addition, it is important by R&D to improve overall construction efficiency by systems analysis, taking into account the influence of design and materials choice on overall construction cost.

12.8.   Project management

12.8.1.   Extract from Task Force Report

In this Report, 'project management' is taken to include activities and relationships between the parties concerned with a project, i.e. client, engineer, contractor and subcontractors; but excludes matters concerned with the internal management of the organisation of each party. It deals, in effect, with overall project management from initial authorisation by the client to completion of payment.

There is a strong need to reappraise existing forms of contract and the relationships and responsibilities between the parties concerned and then to develop more satisfactory forms of contract suitable for work that, often, cannot be fully pre-planned, for work involving a high degree of specialist and sub-contract work, for large interdisciplinary projects, work involving a high degree of unpredictable risk, for work overseas and contracts appropriate to intermediate technology. There is also a need to develop forms of 'turnkey' and 'management' contracts and to establish the relationships and responsibilities between those concerned.

Better data and methods are required for the clients, engineers and contractors to estimate costs more accurately, taking into account the many factors affecting price movements. Methods of bid assessment require re-appraisal and assessment, which may well require changes in standard bills of quantities and conditions of contract.

Effective systems and procedures are needed for communication between client, engineer and contractor and between design office and site, making use of standard computerised systems and improved methods of data transmission. Workable means of programming and monitoring progress and costs are also required.

The requirements for design engineers, technicians, draughtsmen, project managers and workforce are all likely to change substantially during the next 20 years as a result of automated design and drawing systems, improved communication systems, automated measurement and control instruments, social and other factors affecting methods of working, including a probable increase in interdisciplinary and large projects. It is important, therefore, to examine the likely effects of these changes on manpower needs and to re-arrange education and training to meet future requirements.

It is also necessary to develop techniques for the effective training and use of indigenous labour and technicians for work overseas.

12.8.2.   Commentary

Since the Task Force Report was prepared, appraisals have been made of the several types of contract in use — traditional, management, reimbursable — as well as of improved forms dealing with the specialised activities of tunnelling and ground investigation. This is a research activity that should continue to monitor these and any other systems that may develop, in order to examine their advantages and limitations in specific circumstances. The implications of fee-competition for design also require close impartial examination with regard to safety and overall cost effectiveness.

In supporting the Task Force's recommendations for more effective systems and procedures for communication between client, engineer and contractor, the present review draws attention to the need for clarification on matters of legal liability within the various types of contract arrangement, also taking into account the effects of QA procedures.

The provision of more effective communication between all parties in construction is a highly important objective requiring substantial effort on the improvement of data presentation and in the quality of the data themselves, particularly with regard to project control of risk, quality and costs. Better communication of design intentions to site and from the site office to operations is another important objective.

The problem of site safety was neglected in the Task Force Report, but should now be regarded as one of the highest priority areas for attention by R&D and information activities. There are parallel requirements in the achievement of quality and of safety.

The present review supports the Task Force in recommending high priority to the whole area of project management.

12.9.   Concluding remarks

Sections 12.2–12.8 are summaries of the R&D requirements that have been identified and it must be emphasised that the full papers on which these summaries are based should be consulted in Volume 3. Reference should also be made to some other recent reports making recommendation on R&D requirements in some specific areas — for example, the Institution's Report on Coastal Engineering, the Fellowship of Engineering's Report on Irrigation and CIRIA's Report on R&D to Support Overseas Work.

The summary in this Chapter indicates an R&D resources requirement far in excess of that available, or likely to become available, in the UK. This emphasises the need for a national strategy to determine priorities and to make most effective use of resources. In some areas, it will be found that the collection, assessment and presentation of existing information and experience in the form of authoritative guides would be the most cost-effective way forward; but this is a specialist activity requiring considerable resources. In other areas it will be more efficient to rely on R&D results from other countries; but this requires expertise in the area concerned and emphasises the need for a broadly based core of research expertise as being an essential part of the national strategy.

ACKNOWLEDGEMENTS

The ICE Research Sub-Committee wishes to thank the following organisations and individuals for their help and co-operation in its work:

Association of Consulting Engineers
Balfours
Binnie & Partners
British Property Federation
Building Employers Confederation
Building Materials Producers Council
Building Research Establishment
Cement & Concrete Association
Chartered Institute of Building
Chartered Institution of Building Services Engineers
Construction Industry Research & Information Association
Department of the Environment
Engineering and Power Development Consultants Ltd
Federation of Association of Specialist Subcontractors
Federation of Civil Engineering Contractors
G. Maunsell & Partners
Hydraulics Research Limited, Wallingford
Institution of Structural Engineers
Kirk, McClure & Morton
Ministry of Agriculture, Fisheries and Food
National House Building Council
Natural Environment Research Council
NEDO Research Strategy Committee
Newcastle & Gateshead Water Company
Ove Arup & Partners
Peter Fraenkel & Partners
Rofe, Kennard & Lapworth
Royal Institute of British Architects
Royal Institute of Chartered Surveyors
Science and Engineering Research Council
SERC Environment Committee
Sir Alexander Gibb & Partners
Sir Robert McAlpine & Sons Ltd
Sir M. McDonald & Partners
Southern Water
Transport and Road Research Laboratory
Department of Civil Engineering, University of Bristol
Department of Civil Engineering, University of Dundee
Department of Civil Engineering and Building Science, University of
    Edinburgh
Department of Civil Engineering, University of Leeds
Department of Civil Engineering, University of Strathclyde
Water Research Centre
Watson Hawksley
W.S. Atkins Group Consultants
Energy Engineering Group Board
Engineering Management Group Board

Ground Engineering Group Board
Maritime Engineering Group Board
Safety in Civil Engineering Committee
Structural Engineering Group Board
Transportation Engineering Group Board
Water Engineering Group Board

P Ackers; Professor N N Ambraseys; Dr L C Archibald, Professor V Ashkenazi; Professor T Atkinson; P J Balfe; H C Balfour; J N Barber; R Barnsley; Dr S C C Bate; D Bayliss; A D M Bellis; Mrs M Bloom; J B Boden; M E Bramley; S Bratty; M A Brookes; Professor E T Brown; Professor F M Burdekin; W J Carlyle; P J Clark; K W Cole; Dr R D Coombe; J V Corney; R E Coxon; C Craig; R B Croft; D S Currie; F Dawson; D M Deaves; J A Derrington; R H R Douglas; G Duncan; J B L Faulkner, D Fiddes; D B Field; J B Field; Dr C A Fleming; Dr W G K Fleming; Professor G Fleming; I P Gillson; M A W Gooderham; H Goodman; K W Groves; G M Hannah; I W Hannah; M F Hardy; W Harvey; Dr N J Heaf; Professor A W Hendry; B A O Hewett; Dr G D Hobbs; Dr M W Holdgate; R W Horner; C Hotchkiss; R H Hughes; R B Johnson; D A Jolly; A H King; J R A Lang; P Lacey; Dr A S Laughton; E G Mabbs; G Margason; Professor D G McKinlay; G McQuire; Dr W L Mercer; C J Mettem; D W Miles; D S Miller; L Miller; J E Moore; E J Morley; C J E Morris; S N Mustow; Professor P Novak; T O'Brien; H R Oakley; H D Osborn; W Pemberton; J W Phillips; F F Poskitt; D W Quinion; Dr T M Ridley; A D Robb; D G M Roberts; B H Rofe; L Sallabank; Dr R H J Sellin; Dr T L Shaw; J K Smith; Dr S L Smith; P Stalker; E H Taylor; A Taylor; Professor P A Thompson; R L Thompson; S Thorburn; K Tomasin; Dr F Walley; B Wareham; Dr W L Wilkinson; A H Williams; T D Wilson; Dr L R Wootton; H L Yeadon.

CONTENTS OF VOLUME 3 — UPDATED PAPERS FROM 1981 TASK FORCE REPORT: 'LONG-TERM RESEARCH AND DEVELOPMENT REQUIREMENTS IN CIVIL ENGINEERING'

P3 **Coastal Work**
C.A. Fleming, PhD, MICE
(Sir William Halcrow & Partners)

P4 **Commercial and Public Building)**
F. Walley, CB, MSc, PhD, FICE, FIStructE
(Ove Arup & Partners)

P5 **Dams and Reservoirs**
R.E. Coxon, BSc, DIC, FICE, FASCE
(Engineering and Power Development Consultants Ltd)
Also reviewed by
W.J. Carlyle, BSc(Eng), FICE, FIWES
(Binnie & Partners)
Additional material provided by
J.W. Phillips, Bsc(Eng), MICE
Department of the Environment

P6 **Defence Installations**
Maritime, Structural and Transportation
Engineering Group Boards

P7 **Sewerage and Sewage Treatment**
H.R. Oakley, CBE, MSc (Eng), FEng, FICE
(Watson Hawksley)

P8 **Electricity Transmission Structures**
I.P. Gillson, BSc(Eng), DIC, MStructE
(CEGB)

P9 **Gas Installations**
W.L. Mercer, BSc, PhD, FEng, FIGasE, FIM
(British Gas Corporation)

P10 **Hospitals**
R.H. Goodman, DipArch RIBA
(Department of Health and Social Security)

P11 **Housing**
C. Hotchkiss, ARIBA, ARICS
(Robert Matthew, Johnson-Marshall & Partners)

P12 **Hydro-Electric Works**
R.E. Coxon, BSc, DIC, FICE
(Engineering and Power Development Consultants)

P13 **Industrial Building**
C.J.E. Morris, MA, FICE
(W.S. Atkins & Partners)

P14 **Irrigation**
W. Pemberton, BSc, FICE
(Sir Murdoch MacDonald & Partners)

P15 **Mining Works (Surface)**
Professor T. Atkinson, PhD, DIC, FIMinE, FIMM, FIEE, FIMechE
(University of Nottingham)

P16 **Mining Works Underground**
M.A.W. Gooderham, MICE
(Thyssen GB)

P17 **Nuclear Power Stations**
I.W. Hannah, BSc(Tech), FICE
(CEGB)

P18 **Offshore Structures (Gas and Oil)**
M.A. Brookes, BSc(Eng), MICE
(BP International Limited)

P36 **Wind Energy Structures**
C.J.E. Morris, MA, FICE
(W.S. Atkins & Partners)

P37 **Rapid Transit Systems**
T.M. Ridley, CBE, PhD, FICE, FCIT
(London Transport Executive)

P38 **Transportation Planning**
R.D. Coombe, PhD, BTech, MICE, MIHT
(Halcrow Fox & Associates)

P39 **Nuclear Waste Disposal**
W.L. Wilkinson, MA, PhD, FEng, FIChemE
(British Nuclear Fuels)